# The Biochemical Basis
# of Neuropharmacology

New York

Oxford University Press

London Toronto 1974

# The Biochemical Basis of Neuropharmacology

SECOND EDITION

## JACK R. COOPER, Ph.D.

PROFESSOR OF PHARMACOLOGY

YALE UNIVERSITY SCHOOL OF MEDICINE

## FLOYD E. BLOOM, M.D.

CHIEF, LABORATORY OF NEUROPHARMACOLOGY

NATIONAL INSTITUTE OF MENTAL HEALTH

WASHINGTON, D.C.

## ROBERT H. ROTH, Ph.D.

ASSOCIATE PROFESSOR OF PHARMACOLOGY (PSYCHIATRY)

YALE UNIVERSITY SCHOOL OF MEDICINE

COVER:

A composite illustration of various cytological approaches to defining the structural and chemical substrata for the actions of drugs within the brain. At left is diagrammed a theoretical neuron, perikaryon and dendrites above, axon branches, preterminal varicosities, and synaptic terminations below. To the right are illustrated actual micrographs of each of these regions of the central noradrenergic neurons. Upper right: light microscopic autoradiographs of the nucleus locus coeruleus after an interstitial microinjection of $H^3$-proline. Middle right: formaldehyde-induced fluorescence micrograph of the noradrenergic axons within the medial forebrain bundle area. Lower right: electron micrographic appearance of noradrenergic terminals within the forebrain after intraventricular injection of 5-hydroxydopamine, an extremely osmiophilic congener of norepinephrine.

This book is dedicated to the memory
of Nicholas J. Giarman, colleague and dear friend

# Preface
# to the Second Edition

As in the first edition, this book continues to focus on neurotransmitters, proven or probable. In addition to up-dating the information in each chapter, we have split the chapter on catecholamines in two because of the recent spate of findings on dopamine. For similar reasons, new material on the prostaglandins, cyclic AMP, and the cholinergic receptor has been added. Finally, more attention is given to drugs and to neurological diseases. Despite some criticism, we are maintaining our position of listing selected references, chiefly to recent review articles rather than original papers, at the end of each chapter. This derives from our attempt to present in each chapter an overview of what we think are the important aspects of the subject, including serious informational gaps and profitable lines of future research. The interested student should be able to obtain specific references from the review articles that are listed.

Although the book is based on a course given to undergraduate seniors and graduate and medical students at Yale, neurologists and psychiatrists may find some parts useful. We have also been pleasantly surprised to learn that the book has been adopted in undergraduate psychology courses at a number of colleges.

October 1973

J.R.C.
F.E.B.
R.H.R.

# Contents

# The Biochemical Basis
of Neuropharmacology

# 1 | Introduction

NEUROPHARMACOLOGY can be defined simply as the study of drugs that affect nervous tissue. This, however, is not a practical definition since a great many drugs whose therapeutic value is extraneural can affect the nervous system. For example, the cardiotonic drug digitalis will not uncommonly produce central nervous system effects ranging from blurred vision to disorientation. For our purposes we must accordingly limit the scope of neuropharmacology to those drugs specifically employed to affect the nervous system. The domain of neuropharmacology would thus include psychotropic drugs which affect mood and behavior, anesthetics, sedatives, hypnotics, narcotics, anticonvulsants, analeptics, analgetics, and a variety of drugs that affect the autonomic nervous system. Unfortunately, these drugs which are used therapeutically are not curative. They do not eliminate the cause of the disease state but instead merely contain or control the disorder. Thus, for example, convulsive disorders for many individuals represent a life-long problem; the anticonvulsant drugs, when effective, will prevent seizures but will not alter the idiopathic seizure mechanism.

Since, with few exceptions, the precise molecular mechanism of action of these drugs is unknown, and since recitations of their absorption, metabolism, therapeutic indications, and toxic liability can be found in most textbooks of pharmacology, we have chosen to take a different approach to the subject. We will concentrate on the biochemistry and physiology of nervous tissue, emphasizing neurotransmitters, and will introduce the neuropharmacologic agents where their action is related to the subject under discussion. Thus a discussion of LSD is included in the chapter on serotonin (5-hydroxytryptamine [5-HT]) and a suggested mechanism of action of the anti-psychotic drugs in the chapter on the catecholamines.

It is not difficult to justify this focus on either real or proposed neurotransmitters since they act at junctions rather than on the events that occur with axonal conduction or within the cell body. Except for local anesthetics, which appear to interact with axonal membranes, all neuropharmacological agents whose mechanisms of action are to some extent documented seem to be involved primarily with synaptic events. This finding appears quite logical in view of the regulatory mechanisms in the transmission of nerve impulses. Whether a neuron is depolarized or hyperpolarized will depend largely on its excitatory and inhibitory synaptic inputs, and these inputs will in most cases involve neurotransmitters. It can therefore be appreciated that most neuropharmacological agents will exert their action at axo-axonic, axo-dendritic, or axo-somatic junctions. What is enormously difficult to comprehend is the contrast between the action of a drug on a simple neuron causing it either to fire or not to fire, and the wide diversity of central nervous system effects, including subtle changes in mood and behavior, which that same drug will induce.

Studying the molecular mechanisms of action of drugs affecting the nervous system, we can reason that the ultimate effect of these agents must be on ion movements, since the function of the brain is to transmit and store information, its functional unit is the neuron, and neuronal activity is expressed by ion movements across nerve membranes. It should be kept in mind, however, that the psychotropic agents, as well as drugs that affect the autonomic nervous system, appear to exert their primary effect at synapses.

The gap between our descriptive knowledge of neurotropic agents and our knowledge of molecular mechanisms of action of these drugs is wide, and it is pertinent to examine the reasons for the discrepancy. First and foremost is that until quite recently we have been unable to locate, isolate, and characterize receptors for these various drugs. For example, although we can state that the primary site of action of barbiturates is the reticular activating system, and that structure-activity experimentation has given us some idea of the requirements, including spatial configuration, of an active barbiturate, we know very little about the physiology of the reticular activating system and nothing about the presumed attachment of a barbiturate molecule to a synapse in this system. Even more intriguing is the question why such a dramatic specificity exists in neuropharmacology, where, for example, the addition of an extra methyl group on the side chain of pentobarbital changes the compound from a hypnotic drug to a powerful convulsant drug. Even assuming that by some ingenious technique we could isolate the barbiturate receptor (presumably a protein), how would we know that its properties have not changed because of its isolation from the cell? How would we prove that it was indeed the specific receptor for barbiturates? Finally, and the most difficult question, how would we relate this bit of protein to sedation and hypnosis?

Another reason we cannot explain the action of neuropharmacologic agents is that normal and abnormal neural activity at a molecular level have not been explained. And the reason for this deficiency is that biophysical research techniques and approaches of the requisite sophistication have only recently emerged.

The fact, however, that one can find compounds with a specific chemical structure to control a given pathological condition is an exciting experimental finding, since it suggests an approach that the neuropharmacologist can take to clarify normal as well as abnormal brain chemistry and physiology. The use of drugs that affect the adrenergic nervous system has, for instance, uncovered basic and hitherto unknown neural properties such as the uptake, storage, and release of the biogenic amines. The recognition of the analogy between curare poisoning in animals and myasthenia gravis in humans led to the understanding of the cholinergic neuromuscular transmission problem in myasthenia gravis and to subsequent treatment with anticholinesterases. More recently, an investigation of the action of pyrithiamine, an antimetabolite of thiamine, on isolated nerve preparations led to the discovery of the probable cause of the fatal genetic disease, subacute necrotizing encephalomyelopathy. Patients with this disease produce a compound which inhibits the synthesis in the brain of thiamine triphosphate.

The multidisciplinary aspects of pharmacology in general are particularly relevant in the field of neuropharmacology, where a "pure" neurophysiologist or neurochemist would be severely handicapped in elucidating drug action at a molecular level. The neuropharmacologist should be aware of the tools that are available for the total dissection of a biological problem. These would include morphological techniques such as electron microscopy, fluorescence microscopy, and freeze-etching, as well as the classical electrophysiological and biochemical procedures. In addition, if the investigator is concerned with certain aspects of the action of psychotropic drugs, he should have some knowledge of the techniques of behavioral testing.

In science, one measures something. One must know what to measure, where to measure it, and how to measure it. This sounds rather obvious but the student should be aware that, particularly in the neural sciences, these seemingly simple tasks can be enormously difficult. For example, suppose one were interested in elucidating the presumed biochemical aberration in schizophrenia. What would one measure? ATP? Glucose? Ascorbic acid? Unfortunately, this problem has been zealously investigated over the past decade by people who measured everything they could think of, generally in the blood, looking for differences between normal individuals and schizophrenics. As could be predicted, the problem has not been solved. (It may be assumed, however, that these studies have produced a large population of anemic schizophrenics from all the blood-letting.) The situation is the same for a variety of neurological diseases. Even in epilepsy, where there is some evidence that points to a neurochemical lesion, we have no idea what to measure.

Deciding where to measure something in neuroscience is complicated by the heterogeneity of nervous tissue. It is not only a question of which region of the brain to use for the test preparation, but which of the multitude of cell types within each area to choose. If a project involved study of amino acid transport in nervous tissue, for example, would one use isolated nerve ending particles (synaptosomes), glial cells, neuronal cell bodies in culture, a myelinated axon, a ganglion cell? Up to the present time most investigators have used cortical brain slices, but the obvious disadvantage of this preparation is that one has no idea which cellular organelle takes up the amino acid.

How to measure something is a surprisingly easy question to answer, at least if one is dealing with simple molecules. With the recent advances in micro-separation techniques and fluorometric, radiometric, and immunological assays, there is virtually nothing that cannot be measured with a high degree of both specificity and sensitivity. The major problem here is with macromolecules. How can neuronal membranes be isolated and identified, for example, if extraneuronal constituents are an invariable contaminant and if markers to identify unequivocally a neuronal constituent are lacking? The quantitative measurement of receptors is also a key problem (see Chapter 4).

This harangue about measurement is meant to point out that what would on the surface appear to be the simplest part of research can in fact be very difficult. It is for this reason that in each section of this book a critical assessment of research techniques is made. It is vital that students learn not to accept data without an appraisal of the procedures that were employed to obtain the results.

Finally, although the theme is not explicitly dealt with in this book, students may find it educational and often entertaining to attempt to define patterns of research design in neuropharmacology as well as current trends in research areas. One common pattern is for someone to observe something in brain tissue, trace its regional distribution in the brain, and then perform a developmental study of the phenomenon in laboratory animals from prenatal through adult life. Another common pattern is for someone to develop a technique and then search (sometimes with what appears to be desperation) for projects that will utilize the technique. Current trends in the neural sciences include mapping of transmitters in identifiable cells of simple organisms, a search for toxins with specific effects in conduction or transmission, attempts to implicate amino acids as transmitters in the CNS, and the isolation and characterization of receptors.

# 2 | Cellular Foundations of Neuropharmacology

As we begin to consider the particular problems that underlie the analysis of drug actions in the central nervous system, it may be asked, "Just what is so special about nervous tissue?" Nerve cells have two special properties that distinguish them from all other cells in the body. First, they can conduct bioelectric signals for long distances without any loss of signal strength. Secondly, they possess specific intercellular connections with other nerve cells and with innervated tissues such as muscles and glands. These connections determine the types of information a neuron can receive and the range of responses it can yield in return.

## Cytology of the Nerve Cell

We do not need the high resolution of the electron microscope to identify several of the more characteristic structural features of the nerve cell. One of the first observations made with empirical silver impregnation stains such as the Golgi or Cajal stain was that nerve cells are heterogeneous with respect to both size and shape. (One of the confusing features of the nervous system is that each specific region of the brain and each part of each nerve cell not only has its own particular name but often has several synonymous names. So, for example, we find that the nerve cell body is also called the soma and the perikaryon—literally, the part that surrounds the nucleus.)

One of the many ways of classifying nerve cells is in terms of the number of cytoplasmic processes they possess. In the simplest case, the perikaryon has but one process, called an axon; the best examples of this cell type are the sensory fibers whose perikarya occur in groups in the sensory or dorsal root ganglia. In this case, the axon conducts the signal—which was generated by the sensory receptor in the skin or other viscera—centrally through the dorsal root into the spinal cord or cranial nerve nuclei. At the next step of complexity we find neurons possessing two processes: bipolar nerve cells. The sensory receptor nerve cells of the retina, the olfactory mucosa, and the auditory nerve are of this form, as is a certain class of small nerve cells of the brain known as granule cells.

All other nerve cells tend to fall into the class known as multipolar nerve cells. While these cells possess only one axon or efferent conducting process (which may be short or long, branched or straight, and which may possess a recurrent or collateral branch which feeds back onto the same type of nerve cell from which the axon arises), the main differences are in regard to extent and size of the receptive field of the neuron, termed the dendrites or dendritic tree. In silver-stained preparations for the light microscope, the branches of the dendrites look like trees in winter time, although the branches may be long and smooth, short and complex, or bearing short spines like a cactus. It is on these dendritic branches, as well as on the cell body, where the termination of axons from other neurons makes the specialized interneuronal communication point known as the synapse, on which we will later dwell in depth.

When we examine the nerve cell with the electron microscope (Fig. 2-1) and compare it with other cell types whose biology has been well characterized, we find that in general, most nerve cells have very large nuclei in which can be seen one or more nucleoli, believed to be the sites for DNA to RNA transcription. In the cytoplasm of the perikaryon we find both free ribosomes (ribonucleoprotein sites for protein synthesis) as well as multiple cisternae of rough endoplasmic reticulum in which secretory proteins are believed to be manufactured. In addition to the free ribosomes and rough endoplasmic reticulum, we also find a specialized type of smooth endoplasmic reticulum known as the Golgi zone. In the classical secretory cycle of the pancreatic

FIGURE 2-1. Low-power electron micrograph of rat cerebellar cortex. At the lower left, a large neuron can be seen. Its nucleus (Nn), two sets of Golgi apparatus (G), and areas of rough endoplasmic reticulum (RER) can be seen as well as numerous mitochondria (M) and free ribosomes (*). At upper left is the nucleus of an oligodendroglia (Ng); its cytoplasm is scant but numerous free ribosomes can be seen. One prominent nerve terminal (NT) is making specialized contact with the nerve cell. Within the nerve terminals numerous synaptic vesicles and mitochondria can be seen. One myelinated axon is shown in cross section (MA). Also visible in the neuropil are the processes of astrocytes (A) filled with glycogen granules (Gly). Two other nerve terminals (NT) are shown making specialized contacts at upper right with a dendritic spine.

acinar cell, the Golgi zone is the site at which the secretory or-ganelles are packaged into membrane-bound particles for trans-port out of the cell. Nerve cells also possess many mitochondria, the organelle specialized for oxidative phosphorylation. Mitochon-dria of nerves may also be able to incorporate amino acids into proteins, but the functional importance of this synthesis is as yet unexplained.

While the mitochondria occur throughout all parts of the nerve cell and its elongated processes, the rough endoplasmic reticulum is found only in the perikaryon and in the dendrites. The den-drites and the axons both exhibit microtubules, elongated tubular objects 240 Å in diameter whose long axis runs throughout the extent of the axon or dendrite. These microtubules are identical in fine structure to similar organelles found in other cell types in which their function is believed to be cellular support. Although this may be their main function in the elongated cytoplasmic processes of the nerve cell, some scientists have proposed that the microtubules may serve as directional guides for the cytoplasmic transport of cellular ingredients from the cell body to more distal parts of the cell. Microtubules with the same structure and amino acid composition as neuronal microtubules function in the nucleus during mitosis to separate the DNA components of the chromo-somes. Treatment with the drug colchicine will halt both the process of mitosis and that of axoplasmic transport, and will result in a state in which neuronal microtubules become totally disar-rayed. Radioactive colchicine can be shown to bind to solubilized microtubular protein. The drug has been very useful in the exami-nation of the process of axoplasmic transport.

In addition to mitochondria and microtubules, axons also ex-hibit structures called microfilaments. Biochemically, the micro-filaments appear to be composed of the same sub-units as the mi-crotubules although they are organized into a much smaller (100 Å) fibrous structure. Generally, axons which have large numbers of microtubules have very few filaments, and vice versa. Small (i.e. narrow) axons tend to have microtubules but few microfila-ments. Large axons may have many microfilaments but few microtubules. In some cases the microfilaments may extend into the nerve ending, where they tend to form a ring-like configuration around the external perimeter of the nerve-ending axoplasm. Except for the fact that the microfilaments can be stained by silver and probably account for the so-called neurofibrils of classical light microscopy, no specific functions for microfilaments have yet been uncovered.

## The Synapse

The last specialized structural features of the neuron we shall discuss are the contents of the nerve ending and the characteristic specialized contact zone which has been presumptively identified as the site of functional interneuronal communication, i.e. the synapse. As the axon approaches the site of its termination it exhibits structural features not found more proximally (Fig. 2-2). Most striking is the occurrence of large numbers of microvesicles, which have been dubbed synaptic vesicles. These structures tend to be spherical in shape, with diameters varying between 200 and 1200 Å. Depending upon the type of fixation used, the vesicles may exhibit one or more types of internal electron-opaque granularities; this cytochemical characteristic is related to certain endogenous small molecules considered to be potential synaptic transmitting substances (see Chapters 4 and 5). The nerve endings also exhibit mitochondria, but never exhibit microtubules unless the nerve ending belongs to the class of axons possessing several accumulations of synaptic vesicles along their terminal passage. Each of these endings forms a specialized contact with one or more dendritic branches before the ultimate termination. Such endings are known as *en passant* terminals. In this sense, the term "nerve terminal" or "nerve ending" connotes more a functional transmitting site than a structural blind alley.

Electron micrographs of synaptic regions in the central nervous system reveal a specialized contact zone between the axonal nerve ending and the postsynaptic structure. This specialized contact zone is composed of presumed proteinaceous material lining

FIGURE 2-2. High-power view of the same nerve ending seen in Fig. 1. At this magnification the synaptic vesicles can be seen more clearly, as can the zone of specialized contact (Sy). Astrocyte processes containing glycogen (As) can be seen as well as smooth endoplasmic reticulum (SER) and free ribosomes (R) within the cytoplasm of the nerve cell. Note that only about half of the contact between the nerve terminal and the nerve cell membrane exhibits the specialized zone of contact.

the intracellular portions of the pre- and postsynaptic membranes and filling the synaptic cleft between the apposed cell surfaces. Such types of specialized contacts are a general form of the specialized cell contacts seen between many types of cell derived from the embryonic ectoderm, of which the nerve cell is but one.

However, the specialized contact between neurons is polarized: that is, the presynaptic terminal intracellular material is composed of interrupted presynaptic dense projections measuring about 500-700 Å in diameter and separated from each other by distances of 300-400 Å. This material may be present only to bind specific presynaptic nerve endings permanently to specific post-synaptic cell sites. Alternatively, the specialized contact zone could assist in the efficiency of transmission and could constitute one potential method for modulating synaptic transmission in terms of discharge frequency. This is a subject upon which much future research can be expected.

## Functional Interpretations from Cytology

If we were to try to infer the functions of a neuron from the foregoing catalogue of its cellular machinery, we would be entitled to the following assumptions. Despite wide variations in cell shape, size, and volume, most nerve cells possess large amounts of unattached ribosomes, presumably for the synthesis of intracellular materials such as enzymes and structural macromolecules. However, the cell body is also filled with varying quantities of rough endoplasmic reticulum and smooth endoplasmic reticulum indicative of cells that package synthetic material for transcellular secretion. Thus, we anticipate the neuron to be a dynamic secretory cell with broad synthetic capabilities.

While organelles with such synthesizing capabilities characterize both the dendrite and cell body cytoplasm, they are never found within the axon. Since the axon possesses no apparent synthetic capacity of its own, other mechanisms have had to be developed to explain the way in which the axon can maintain its vitality. One such proposal is that the cell body synthesizes all the required macromolecules for the axon and that a process of somatofugal transport carries them from the cell body down the axon. This theory of axoplasmic transport has been substantiated by studies involving actual physical barriers to intra-axonal movement and by labeling proteins in the cell body to time their rates of migration toward the periphery. Such studies have indicated that the flow rates may vary from as little as one-tenth of a millimeter to 400 millimeters per day, depending upon the organelle or metabolite used as a tracer and the type of axonal system studied.

Regardless of the rate at which macromolecules can be transported down the axon, certain actions of the nerve terminal, such as the release of transmitter, occur at rates which still exceed the amount arriving from the perikaryon. In these cases, the nerve terminals have acquired the necessary enzymes in order to synthesize the transmitters *de novo* from amino acids present in the extracellular fluid spaces. Nerve terminals are specialized functionally in yet another way which helps to decrease their need for transmitter synthesis: almost all neurochemical types of nerve terminal, except those releasing acetylcholine, are able to actively re-accumulate the transmitter they release. In the case of the cholinergic synapse, choline is taken up by the presynaptic terminal. The active re-uptake process is in general a high affinity and relatively low capacity specific uptake system which is energy- and sodium-dependent. Drugs that have selective action on the re-uptake mechanism can produce functional changes in the time course of synaptic action by prolonging the survival of the transmitter near the receptor before re-accumulation or catabolism removes the molecules. Exploitation of the re-uptake process is essential to all forms of autoradiographic localization and to the action of drugs which produce chemical sympathectomy, such as 6-hydroxydopamine (see Chapter 5).

*Glia*

A second element in the maintenance of the axon's integrity depends on a type of cell known as neuroglia, which we have not yet discussed. There are two main types of neuroglia. The first is called the fibrous astrocyte, a descriptive term based on its starlike shape in the light microscope and on the fibrous nature of its cytoplasmic organelles, which can be seen in both light and electron microscopy. The astrocyte is found mainly in regions of axons and dendrites and tends to surround or contact the adventitial surface of blood vessels. Functions such as insulation (between conducting surfaces) and organization (to surround and separate functional units of nerve endings and dendrites) have been empirically attributed to the astrocyte, mainly on the basis of its structural characteristics.

The second type of neuroglia is known as the oligodendrocyte. It is called the satellite cell when it occurs close to nerve cell bodies, and the Schwann cell when it occurs in the peripheral nervous system. The cytoplasm of the oligodendrocyte is characterized by rough endoplasmic reticulum but its most prominent characteristic is the enclosure of concentric layers of its own surface membrane around the axon. These concentric layers come together so closely that the oligodendrocyte cytoplasm is completely squeezed out and the original internal surfaces of the membrane become fused, presenting the ring-like appearance of the myelin sheath in cross section (Fig. 2-1). Along the course of an axon, which may be many centimeters in length, many oligodendrocytes are required to constitute its myelin sheath. At the boundary between adjacent portions of the axon covered by separate oligodendrocytes, there is an uncovered axonal portion known as the node of Ranvier.

Many central axons and certain elements of the peripheral autonomic nervous system do not possess myelin sheaths. Even these axons, however, are not bare and exposed to the extracellular fluid, but rather they are enclosed within single invaginations of the oligodendrocyte surface membrane. Because of this close relationship between the conducting portions of the nerve cell, its axon, and the oligodendrocyte, it is easy to see the origin of the proposition that the oligodendrocyte may contribute to the nurture of the nerve cell. While this idea may be correct, no evidence is yet available. Clearly, the glia are incapable of supporting the axon when it has been severed from the cell body, for example, by trauma or by surgically induced lesioning. This incapacity is fortuitous for neuroscientists, since one of the chief methods of defining nerve circuits within the brain has been the staining of degenerating axons following brain lesions.

*Brain Permeability Barriers*

While the unique cytological characteristics of neurons and glia are sufficient to establish the complex intercellular relationships of the brain, there is yet another histophysiologic concept to consider. Numerous chemical substances pass from the bloodstream into the brain at rates which are far slower than for entry into all other organs in the body. There are similar slow rates of transport between the cerebrospinal fluid and the brain, although there is no good standard in other organs against which to compare this latter movement.

These permeability barriers appear to be the end result of numerous contributing factors which present diffusional obstacles to chemicals on the basis of molecular size, charge, solubility, and specific carrier systems. The difficulty has not been in establishing the existence of these barriers, but rather in determining their mechanisms. When the relatively small protein ($MW = 43,000$) horseradish peroxidase is injected intravenously into mice, its location within the tissue can be demonstrated histochemically with the electron microscope. As opposed to the easy transvascular movement of this substance across muscle capillaries, in brain the peroxidase molecule is unable to penetrate through the continuous layer of vascular endothelial cells. The endothelial cells of brain capillaries differ from those of other tissue such as muscle and heart in that the intercellular zones of membrane apposition are much more highly developed in the brain, and are virtually continuous along all surfaces of these cells. Furthermore, cerebral vascular endothelial cells show a distinct lack of pinocytotic vesicles which have been related to transvascular carrier systems of both large and small molecules.

Since the enzyme marker can neither go through or between the endothelial cells, an operationally defined barrier exists. Whether the same barrier is also applicable to highly charged lipophobic small molecules cannot be determined from these observations. As neuropharmacologists, what concerns us most here are the factors which retard the entrance of these smaller molecules, such as norepinephrine and serotonin, their amino acid precursors, or drugs which affect the catabolism or synthesis of these two neurotransmitters. For these substances, the poorly conceived and minimally studied barriers may be tentatively considered as solvent partitions across the vasculature, since many such molecules when permitted entry via the cerebrospinal fluid, are able to diffuse widely through the extracellular spaces of the brain. While these extracellular spaces were long interpreted as exceedingly small on the basis of electron micrographs, we now know that the lack of space was an artifact due to swelling of astrocytes during fixation. Thus, once a substance can enter the perivascular extracellular spaces of the brain, it is likely to encounter few barriers which would prevent it from migrating between cells—presumably along concentration gradients, but possibly moved by specific carriers—to reach those neurons or glia capable of incorporating it, responding to it, or metabolizing it.

The barriers are not one-way, since those same substances which find it difficult to get into the brain also find it exceedingly difficult to leave. Thus, when the monoamines are increased in concentration by the blocking of their catabolic pathways (see Chapter 5), the high levels of amine persist until the inhibiting agents are metabolized or excreted. One such route is the "acid transport" system by which the choroid plexus and/or brain parenchymal cells actively secrete acid catabolites. This step can be blocked by the drug probenecid, resulting in increased brain and CSF catabolites of the amines.

Since the precise nature of these barriers can still not be formulated, the student would be wise to avoid the "great wall of China" concept and lean toward the possibility of a series of variously placed, progressively selective filtration sites, which discriminate substances on the basis of several molecular characteristics. With lipid soluble, weak electrolytes, a characteristic of most centrally acting drugs, transport occurs by a process of passive diffusion. Thus, a drug will penetrate the cell only in the undissociated form and at a rate consonent with its lipid solubility and its pKa.

## BIOELECTRIC PROPERTIES OF THE NERVE CELL

With these structural details as a background, we can now turn to the best-known feature of the nerve cell, namely, its bioelectric property. However, even for an introductory presentation such as this, we must understand certain basic concepts of the physical phenomena of electricity in order to have a working knowledge of the bioelectric characteristics of living cells.

The initial concept to grasp is that of a difference in potential existing within a charged field, as occurs when charged particles are separated and prevented from randomly redistributing themselves. When a potential difference exists, the amount of charge per unit of time which will flow between the two sites (that is, current flow) depends upon the resistance separating them. If the resistance tends to zero, no net current will flow since no potential difference can exist in the absence of a measurable resistance. If the resistance is extremely high, only a minimal current will flow and that will be proportional to the electromotive force or potential difference between the two sites. The relationship between voltage, current, and resistance is the famous Ohm's law, expressed as: $V = I \cdot R$.

When we come to the measurement of the electrical properties of living cells, these basic physical laws apply, but with one exception. The pioneer electrobiologists, who did their work before the discovery and definition of the electron, developed a convention for the flow of charges based not on the electron but on the flow of positive charges. Therefore, since in biological systems the flow of charges is not carried by electrons but by ions, the direction of flow is expressed in terms of movement of positive charges. To analyze the electrical potentials of a living system, we use small electrodes (a microprobe for detecting current flow or potential), electronic amplifiers for increasing the size of the current or potential, and oscilloscopes or polygraphs for displaying the potentials observed against a time base.

FIGURE 2-3. At the top is shown a hypothetical neuron (Nl) receiving a single excitatory pathway (E) and a single inhibitory pathway (I). A stimulating electrode (S) has been placed on the nerve cell's axon; microelectrode 1 is extracellular to nerve cell 1, while microelectrode 2 is in the cell body, and microelectrode 3 is in its nerve terminal. Microelectrode 4 is recording from within postsynaptic cell 2. The potentials and current, recorded by each of these electrodes, are being compared through a "black box" of electronics with a distant extracellular grounded electrode, and displayed on an oscilloscope screen. When the cell is resting and the electrode is on the outside of the cell, no poten-

*Membrane Potentials*

If we take two electrodes and place them on the outside of a living cell or tissue, we will find little, if any, difference in potential. However, if we injure a cell so as to break its membrane or insert one ultra-fine electrode across the membrane, we will find a potential difference such that the inside of the cell is 50 or more millivolts negative with respect to the extracellular electrode (Fig.

---

tial difference is observed (1). In the resting state, electrode 2 records a steady potential difference between inside and outside of approximately minus 50 millivolts (2). While recording from electrode 2 and stimulating the inhibitory pathway, the membrane potential is hyperpolarized during the inhibitory postsynaptic potential (2 + I). When recording from electrode 2 and stimulating the excitatory pathway, a subthreshold stimulus (St) produced an excitatory postsynaptic potential indicated by a brief depolarization of the resting membrane potential (2 + E). When the excitatory effects are sufficient to reach threshold (T), an action potential is generated which reverses the inside negativity to inside positivity (2 + E). On the lower scale, potentials recorded by electrodes 3 and 4 are compared on the same time-base following axonal stimulation of nerve cell 1. The point of stimulus is seen as an electrical artifact at point S. The action potential generated at the nerve terminal occurs after a finite lag period due to the conduction time (c) of the axon between the stimulating electrode and the nerve terminal. The action potential in the nerve ending does not directly influence postsynaptic cell 2 until after the transmitter has been liberated and can react with nerve cell 2's membrane, causing the excitatory postsynaptic potential indicated by the dotted line. The time between the beginning of the action potential recorded by microelectrode 3 and the excitatory postsynaptic potential recorded by electrode 4 (A) is the time required for excitation secretion coupling in the nerve terminal and the liberation of sufficient transmitter to produce effects on nerve cell 2.

2-3). This transmembrane potential difference is found in almost all types of living cells in which it has been sought; such a membrane is said to be electrically polarized. By passing negative ions into the cell through the microelectrode (or extracting cations), the inside can be made more negative (hyperpolarized). If positive current is applied to the inside of the cell the transmembrane potential difference is decreased, and the potential is said to be depolarized. The potential difference across the membrane of most living cells can be accounted for by the relative distribution of the intracellular and extracellular ions.

The extracellular fluid is particularly rich in sodium and relatively low in potassium. Inside the cell, the cytoplasm is relatively high in potassium content and very low in sodium. While the membrane of the cell permits potassium ions ($K^+$) to flow back and forth with relative freedom, it resists the movement of the sodium ions ($Na^+$) from the extracellular fluid to the inside of the cell. Since the potassium ions can cross the membrane they tend to flow along the concentration gradient—which is highest inside the cell. Potassium diffusion out of the cell leaves a relative negative charge behind due to the negative charges of the macromolecular proteins. As the negative charge inside the cell begins to build up, the further diffusion of potassium from inside to outside is retarded. Eventually an equilibrium point will be reached which is proportional to certain physical constants and to the relative concentrations of intracellular and extracellular potassium and chloride ions. These features apply generally, not only to nerve and muscle cells but also to red blood cells, gland cells, and other cells large enough to have their transmembrane potential measured.

### Membrane Leaks and Pumps

When the nerve cell or muscle fiber can be placed in a dish and transmembrane potential recordings made, the relation between the membrane potential and external potassium concentration can be directly tested by exchanging the extracellular fluid for artificial solutions of varying potassium concentration. When this experiment is performed on muscle cells, we find that the membrane potential bears a linear relationship to the log of the external potassium concentration at normal to high potassium concentrations, but deviates from this linear relationship when the external potassium concentration is less than normal. To account for this discrepancy we must now re-examine an earlier statement. While the plasma membranes of nerve and muscle cells and other types of polarized cells are relatively impermeable to the flow of sodium ions along the high concentration gradient from extracellular to intracellular, they are not completely impermeable. With radio-isotope experiments it can be established that a certain amount of sodium leaks into the resting cell from outside. The amount of measurable sodium leakage into the cell occurs at a rate sufficient to double the intracellular sodium concentration in approximately one hour if there were not some opposing process to maintain the relatively low intracellular sodium concentration. The process which continuously maintains the low intracellular sodium concentration is known as active sodium transport, or colloquially as the "sodium pump." This pump mechanism ejects sodium from the inside of the cell against the high concentration and electrical gradients forcing it in. However, the "pump" does not handle sodium exclusively but requires the presence of extracellular potassium, so that when a sodium ion is ejected from the cell, a potassium ion is incorporated into the cell.

When the external potassium concentration is near normal, the transmembrane potential, which is based mainly on potassium concentration differences, behaves as if there were actually more extracellular potassium than really exists. This is because the sodium-potassium exchange mechanism elevates the amount of potassium coming into the cell. Remember that potassium permeability is relatively high and that potassium will tend to diffuse out of the cell because of its concentration gradient but to diffuse into the cell because of charge attraction. Therefore, two factors operate to drive potassium into the cell in the presence of relatively low external potassium concentration: (1) the electrical gradient across the membrane and (2) the sodium-potassium pump mechanism. The latter system could be considered "electrogenic" since at low external $K^+$ concentrations it modifies the electrical status of the muscle membrane. Other metabolic pumps operate simply to exchange cationic species across the membrane and are "non-electrogenic." The relative "electrogenicity" of a pump may depend on the ratio of the exchange cations (i.e. 1 : 1 or 2 : 1, or 3 : 2). The pump is immediately dependent upon metabolic energy and can be blocked by several metabolic poisons such as dinitrophenol and the rapid acting cardiac glycoside, ouabain.

## The Uniqueness of Nerve

All that we have said regarding the transmembrane ionic distributions applies equally as well to the red blood cell membrane as to the nerve membrane. Thus, the possession of a transmembrane potential difference is not sufficient to account for the bioelectric properties of the nerve cell. The essential difference between the red blood cell and the nerve cell can be brought out by applying depolarizing currents across the membrane. When the red blood cell membrane is depolarized, the difference in potential across the cell passively follows the imposed polarization. However, when a nerve cell membrane, such as the giant axon of an invertebrate, is depolarized from a resting value of approximately $-70$ millivolts to approximately $-10$ to $-15$ millivolts, an explosive self-limiting process occurs by which the transmembrane potential is reduced not merely to zero but overshoots zero, so that the inside of the membrane now becomes positive with respect to the outside. This overshoot may extend for 10 to 30 millivolts in the positive direction. Because of this explosive response to an electrical depolarization the nerve membrane is said to be electrically excitable, and the resultant explosion is known as the action potential.

## Analysis of Action Potentials

In an elegant series of now classical pioneering experiments, Hodgkin, Huxley, and Katz were able to analyze the various ionic steps responsible for the action potential. When the cell begins to depolarize from stimulation current, the current flow across the membrane is carried by potassium. As the membrane becomes more depolarized, the conductance across the membrane to sodium (conductance is the inverse expression of resistance) increases and more sodium flows into the cell along its electrical and concentration gradients. As sodium flows in, the membrane becomes more and more depolarized which further increases the conductance to sodium, further depolarizing the membrane at a greater rate. This self-perpetuating process continues, driven by the flow of sodium ions tending toward their equilibrium distribution, which should be proportional to the original extracellular and intracellular concentrations of sodium.

However, the peak of the action potential does not attain the equilibrium potential predicted on the basis of transmembrane sodium concentrations because of a second phase of events. The electrical process which leads to the rapidly increasing conductance to sodium also further increases the transmembrane conductance to potassium, whose flow then also increases along its concentration gradient, that is, from inside to outside the cell. This process restricts the height of the reversal potential since it tends to maintain the inside negativity of the cell and also begins to reduce the membrane conductance to sodium, thus making the action potential a self-limiting phenomena. In most nerve axons, the action potential lasts for approximately 0.2 to 0.5 milliseconds, depending on the type of fiber and the temperature in which it is measured.

Once the axon has reached threshold, the action potential will be propagated at a rate which is proportional to the diameter of the axon and which is further accelerated by the presence of the glial myelin sheaths, which restrict the active conducting points to the node of Ranvier. As mentioned above, these are the only sites on the myelinated axons at which the axonal membrane is directly exposed to the extracellular fluid and thus are the only sites at which transmembrane ionic flows can take place. Therefore, instead of the action potential propagating from minutely contiguous sites of the membrane, the action potential in the myelinated axon leaps from node to node. This saltatory conduction is consequently much more rapid.

The threshold level for an all-or-none action potential is also inversely proportional to the diameter of the axon: large myelinated axons respond to low values of imposed stimulating current, whereas fine and unmyelinated axons require much greater depolarizing currents. Local anesthetics appear to act by blocking activation of the sodium conductance preventing depolarization.

Once threshold has been reached, a complete action potential will be developed unless it occurs too quickly after a preceding action potential, during the so-called refractory phase. This phase varies for different types of excitable nerve and muscle cells and appears to be related to the activation process increasing sodium conductance, a phenomenon which has a finite cycling period; that is, the membrane cannot be reactivated before a finite interval of time has occurred. Potassium conductance increases with the action potential and lasts slightly longer than the activation of sodium conductance. This results in a prolonged phase of after-hyperpolarization due to the continued redistribution of potassium from inside to outside the membrane. If the axonal membrane is artificially maintained at a transmembrane potential equal to the potassium equilibrium potential, no after-hyperpolarization can be seen.

### Junctional Transmission

While these ionic mechanisms appear to account adequately for the phenomena occurring in the propagation of action potential down an axon, they do not *per se* explain what happens when the action potential reaches the nerve ending. At the nerve ending the membrane of the axon is separated from the membrane of the postjunctional nerve cell, muscle, or gland by an intercellular space of 50-200 Å (Fig. 2-2). In those cases in which an electrode can be placed in both the terminal axon and the postsynaptic cell, depolarization of the nerve terminal does not usually result in a direct and instantaneous shift in the transmembrane potential of the postsynaptic element. Thus, the junctional site seldom appears to have the properties of direct electrical excitability described above for the axon.

## Axons versus Junctions

Junctional or synaptic transmission varies in certain important characteristics from axonal transmission. Firstly, impulses travel in only one direction across synaptic or junctional sites. In this regard the junction can be said to be a rectifier or valve permitting only one direction of flow. In the axon, impulses can be made to travel in the proper (or orthodromic) direction from receptor to axon terminal; however, if the distal end of an axon is stimulated and recordings made from its cell body, the action potential will also travel backward up the axon. This is known as antidromic activation.

We have already mentioned that the depolarization of the postjunctional cell is separated in time by at least 0.1 to 0.2 msec from activity in the presynaptic terminal. This transmission delay time cannot be accounted for simply on the basis of the electrical resistance and capacitance between the junctional elements and suggests that a separate and nonelectrical process occurs at the transmission site. No such delays are seen with conduction down the axon (see above). Transmission across junctional sites has finite temporal limits and the postsynaptic element cannot usually follow the presynaptic element at stimulation rates higher than 100/sec. Junctional sites are also extremely sensitive to drugs and hypoxia. On the other hand, axonal transmission can follow stimulation rates as high as 1500/sec at which time they are limited only by the relative refractory period of the axon.

A final distinguishing characteristic between junctional and axonal transmission is that subthreshold presynaptic stimuli can combine in time to lead to a threshold stimulus and produce firing. This is due to the fact that subthreshold potential changes have a prolonged electrotonic spread; second subthreshold stimulus can have a cumulative effect upon the residua of a previous declining subthreshold stimulus. On the other hand, in axons, action potentials are either all-or-none, and no such temporal summation can be demonstrated. Temporal summation can result in the postsynaptic cell continuing to discharge for several msec after the stimulation of the presynaptic element has stopped. Firing in the axon begins and ends with the imposed stimulation, and normally no after-discharges occur.

*Postsynaptic Potentials*

With the advent of microelectrode techniques for recording the transmembrane potential of nerve cells *in vivo*, it was possible to determine the effects of stimulation of nerve pathways which had previously been shown to cause either excitation or inhibition of synaptic transmission. From just such studies Eccles and his colleagues observed that subthreshold excitatory stimuli would produce postsynaptic potentials with time durations of 2 to 20 msec. The excitatory postsynaptic potentials could algebraically summate both with the excitatory and inhibitory postsynaptic potentials. Most importantly, the duration of these postsynaptic potentials was longer than could be accounted for on the basis of electrical activity in the preterminal axon or on the electrotonic conductive properties of the postsynaptic membrane (Fig. 2-3). This latter observation combined with the fact that synaptic sites are not directly electrically excitable provides the conclusive evidence that central synaptic transmission must be chemical: the prolonged time course is compatible with a rapidly released chemical transmitter whose time course of action is terminated by local enzymes, diffusion, and re-uptake by the nerve ending.

By such experiments it was possible to work out the basic ionic mechanisms for inhibitory and excitatory postsynaptic potentials. When an excitatory pathway is stimulated, the presynaptic element liberates an excitatory transmitter which is able to activate the ionic conductance of the postsynaptic membrane. This leads to a generalized increase in all transmembrane ionic conductances, forcing the membrane to move toward the sodium equilibrium potential; in the resting state, as has already been discussed, the membrane resides near the potassium equilibrium potential. The approach to the sodium equilibrium potential results in depolarization, and if this is sufficient to reach the threshold for adjacent electrically excitable portions of the cell membrane, an all-or-none action potential will result. If the resultant depolarization is insufficient to reach firing threshold, the cell may still discharge if additional excitatory postsynaptic potentials summate adequately before the first excitatory potential has disappeared.

The inhibitory postsynaptic potential resulting from the stimulation of an inhibitory pathway to the postsynaptic cell has been explained in terms of the fact that inhibitory transmitter is able selectively to activate conductance for chloride, resulting in an inward diffusion of this ion and a further hyperpolarization of the membrane. This counter-balances the excitatory postsynaptic potentials.

Because the sites of synaptic or junctional transmission are electrically inexcitable, the postsynaptic membrane potential can be maintained at various levels by applying current through intracellular electrodes and changing the intracellular concentrations of various ions. By such maneuvers, it is possible to poise the membrane at or near the so-called equilibrium potentials for each of the ionic species and to determine the ionic species whose equilibrium potential corresponds to the conductance change caused by the synaptic transmitter. This is the most molecular test for the identification of actions of a synaptic transmitter substance. (However, certain objections can be raised to this test in terms of those nerve endings making junctional contacts on distal portions of the dendritic tree. Here, the postsynaptic potentials may be incompletely transmitted to the cell body in which the recording electrode is placed.)

*Slow Postsynaptic Potentials*

Most of the postsynaptic potentials described by Eccles and his colleagues were relatively short, usually 20 msec or less and appear to result from passive changes in ionic conductance. Recently postsynaptic potentials of slow onset and several seconds' duration have been described (Fig. 2-3), both of a hyperpolarizing nature and of a depolarizing nature. While such prolonged postsynaptic potentials could be due either to a prolonged release of transmitter or to a persistence of the transmitter at postsynaptic receptor sites, there is substantial support for the possibility that slow postsynaptic potentials could also be caused by other forms of synaptic communication. Many of these slower synaptic potentials are not accompanied by the expected increase in transmembrane ionic conductances, but are instead accompanied by increased transmembrane ionic impedance. The most simple explanations for membrane potential changes accompanied by increased membrane resistance are: (a) that the effect is generated at a "presynaptic" site whereby tonically active excitatory or inhibitory synapses are inactivated by synapses on their terminals; (b) that the action of the transmitter released by a slow synapse is to inactivate a normal finite resting conductance, such as that of sodium or potassium. Since most of the sites where slow synaptic potentials have been observed do not fulfill the anatomical prerequisite of axo-axonic presynaptic synapses, the second explanation may be more likely. A third explanation for such potentials has also been advanced, namely, that the transmitter activates an electrogenic pump mechanism, that is, a metabolically driven ionic "pump" which exchanges unequal numbers of similarly charged ions across the membrane. Studies on invertebrate neurons indicate that such electrogenic mechanisms should have several distinguishable properties: they should be virtually independent of the distribution of the ions to be pumped; they should not exhibit an equilibrium potential; they should be temperature dependent; and they should be sensitive to metabolic poisons and uncouplers of oxidative phosphorylation. Such data are extremely complex to analyze as several membrane properties also include temperature dependency and metabolic poison sensitivity. Thus, at the present time, a true electrogenic synapse in the mammalian central nervous system remains to be described. However, it also seems likely that transmitters such as the catecholamines can activate the synthesis of cyclic nucleotides, which in turn can activate intraneuronal protein kinases that can phosphorylate specific membrane proteins. The phosphorylation of a membrane protein could be expected to alter its ionic permeability, and perhaps such changes lie at the root of the membrane effects of several types of neurotransmitters.

*Transmitter Secretion*

We have already seen that the cellular machinery of the neuron suggests it functions as a secretory cell. The secretion of synaptic transmitters is the activity-locked expression of neuronal activity induced by the depolarization of the nerve terminal. Recently, it has been possible to separate the excitation-secretion coupling process of the presynaptic terminal into at least two distinct phases. This has been made possible through an analysis of the action of the puffer fish poison tetrodotoxin, which blocks the electrical excitation of the axon but does not block the release of transmitter substance from the depolarized nerve terminal. The best of such experiments have been performed in the giant synaptic junctions of the squid stellate ganglion, in which the nerve terminals are large enough to be impaled by recording and stimulating microelectrodes, and recording from the postsynaptic ganglion neurons. In this case, when tetrodotoxin blocks conduction of action potentials down the axon, electrical depolarization of the presynaptic terminal still results in the appearance of an excitatory postsynaptic potential in the ganglion neuron. Since the action of tetrodotoxin appears to be relatively selective for the early activation of increase in $Na^+$ conductance, the excitation secretion may be coupled more closely to the process causing the delayed increase in $K^+$ conductance. However, $Ca^{++}$ must also be present in sufficient concentration or no release will occur. Although the long-distance conducting portions of mammalian central neurons appear to be electrically excitable, the points at which nerve cells communicate now appear to be exclusively chemical.

Biochemical, ultrastructural, and physiological experiments have led to the concept that transmitter molecules are stored within vesicles in the nerve terminal, and that the Ca-dependent excitation-secretion coupling within the deplorized nerve terminal requires the transient exchange of vesicular contents into the synaptic cleft. It is unclear whether the vesicle simply undergoes a rapid fusion with the presynaptic specialized membrane to allow the transmitter stored in the vesicle to diffuse out, or whether the process of exocytotic release simultaneously requires the insertion of the vesicle membrane into the synaptic plasma membrane, reappearing later by the reverse process, namely, endocytosis. Information on the lipid and protein components of the two types of membranes suggests that there are too many differences to allow for long-term fusion-endocytosis cycles, but rapid fusion or perhaps contact exocytosis seems a likely prospect. In noradrenergic vesicles, the transmitter is stored in very high concentrations, presumably in some form of ternary complexes involving ATP, Ca, and possibly additional lipids or lipoproteins. Unfortunately, vesicles from central synapses have never been completely purified, and therefore all such analyses remain somewhat open to interpretation. The vesicle story is further discussed in Chapter 4.

### An Approach to Neuropharmacological Analysis

You can now see that the business of analyzing bioelectrical potentials can be very complicated even when restricted to the changes in single neurons or in small portions of contiguous neurons. But if we restrict our examination of centrally-active drugs to analyses of effects on single cells we can ask rather precise questions. For example, does drug "X" act on resting membrane potential or resistance, on an electrogenic pump, or on the sodium- or potassium-activation phase of the action potential, or does it act by blocking or modulating the effects of junctional transmission between two specific groups of cells.

Unfortunately, both for us and for the literature, we have had these precise electrophysiological tools for less than ten years.

Therefore earlier neuropharmacologists were required to examine effects of the drug on populations of nerve cells. This was usually done in one of two ways. Large macroelectrodes were employed to measure the potential difference between one brain region and another. These electroencephalograms reflect mainly the moment to moment algebraic and spatial summations of slow synaptic potentials, and almost none of their electrical activity is due to actual action potentials generated by individual neurons (unit discharges). A second type of analysis was based on evoked responses, in which macroelectrodes recorded the potential changes occurring when a gross sensory stimulation (such as a flash of light or a quick sound) was delivered. Changes in recordings from cortical or subcortical sites along the sensory pathway were then sought during the action of a drug. While we can criticize the technical and interpretative shortcomings of such methods of central drug analysis, these methods were able to reflect the population response of a group of neurons to a drug, something which single unit analysis can do only after many single recordings are collated.

APPROACHES

If, as modern-day neuropharmacologists, we are chiefly concerned with uncovering the mechanisms of action of drugs in the brain, there are several avenues along which we can organize our attack: We could choose to examine the way in which drugs influence the perception of sensory signals by higher intergrative centers of the brain; this is compatible with a single neuron and ionic conductance type of analysis, such as how do drugs affect inhibitory postsynaptic potentials. Drugs which cause convulsions, such as strychnine, have been analyzed in this respect, but all types of inhibitory postsynaptic potential are not affected by strychnine.

A second basic approach would be to use both macroelectrodes and microelectrodes to compare the drug response of single units and populations of units in the same brain region. However, this approach is clearly limited unless we understand the intimate functional relations between the multiple types of cells found even within one region of the brain.

A third approach is also possible. We could choose to separate the effects of drugs between those affecting generation of the action potential and its propagation, and those acting on junctional transmission. For this type of analysis, we must identify the chemical synaptic transmitter for the junctions to be studied. Many of the interpretative problems already alluded to can be attacked through this approach. Thus, as you may expect, there is likely to be more than one type of excitatory and inhibitory transmitter substance, and a convulsant drug might affect the response to one type of inhibitory transmitter without affecting another. Moreover, a drug might have specific regional effects in the brain if it could affect a unique synaptic transmitter there. In fact, using this approach it might be possible to find drug effects not directly reflected in electrical activity at all, but related more to the catabolic or anabolic systems maintaining the required functional levels of transmitter. We shall conclude this chapter by considering the techniques for identifying the synaptic transmitter for particular synaptic connections. The chapters which follow are organized to present in detail our current understanding of putative central neurotransmitter substances.

IDENTIFICATION OF SYNAPTIC TRANSMITTERS

How then, do we identify the substance released by nerve endings? The entire concept of chemical junctional transmission arose from the classical experiments of Otto Loewi, who demonstrated chemical transmission by transferring the ventricular fluid of a stimulated frog heart onto a nonstimulated frog heart, thereby showing that the effects of the nerve stimulus on the first heart were reproduced by the chemical activity of the solution flowing onto the second heart. Since the phenomenon of chemical transmission originated from studies of peripheral autonomic organs, these peripheral junctions have become convenient model systems for central neuropharmacological analysis.

Certain interdependent criteria have been developed to identify junctional transmitters. By common-sense analysis, one would suspect that the most important criterion would be that a substance suspected of being a junctional transmitter must be demonstrated to be released from the prejunctional nerve endings when the nerve fibers are selectively stimulated. This criterion was relatively easily satisfied for isolated autonomic organs where only one or at most two nerve trunks enter the tissue, and the whole system can be isolated in an organ bath. In the central nervous system, however, satisfaction of this criterion presumes: (a) that the proper nerve trunk or set of nerve axons can be selectively stimulated and (b) that release of the transmitter can be detected in the amounts released by single nerve endings after one action potential. This last subcriterion is necessary since we wish to restrict our analysis to the first set of activated nerve endings and not examine the substances released by the secondary and tertiary interneurons in the chain, some of which might reside quite close to the primary endings. The biggest problem with this criterion in the brain, however, is the lack of a method for detecting release which does not in itself destroy the functional and structural integrity of the region of the brain being analyzed. Such techniques as internally perfused cannulae or surface suction cups are chemically at the same level of resolution as the evoked potential and the cortical electroencephalogram: each of these methods records the resultant activity of thousands if not millions of nerve endings and synaptic potentials. Release has also been studied in brain slices incubated in "physiological buffer solutions" *in vitro*. While these techniques can demonstrate the effects of very large electrical depolarizing potentials, the relationship of a brain slice to the living brain remains to be determined.

## Localization

Because it is difficult, if not impossible, to identify the substance released from single nerve endings by selective stimulation, the next-best evidence might be to prove that a suspected synaptic transmitter resides in the presynaptic terminal of our selected nerve pathway. Normally, we would expect that the enzymes for synthesizing and catabolizing this substance should also be in the vicinity of this nerve ending, if not actually part of the nerve ending cellular machinery. For satisfaction of this criterion, several types of specific cytochemical methods for both light microscopy and electron microscopy have been developed. More commonly employed is the biochemical population approach, analyzing the regional concentrations of suspected synaptic transmitter substances. However, presence *per se* indicates neither release-ability nor neuro-effectiveness (e.g. acetylcholine in the nerve-free placenta or serotonin in the enterochromaffin cell).

*Synaptic Mimicry: Drug Injections*

A third criterion arising from the peripheral autonomic nervous system analysis is that the suspected exogenous substance mimics the action of the transmitter released by nerve stimulation. In most pharmacological studies of the nervous system, drugs are administered intravascularly or onto one of the external or internal surfaces of the brain. The substances could also be directly injected into a given region of the brain although the resultant structural damage would have to be controlled and the target verified histologically. The analysis of the effects of drugs given by each of these various gross routes of administration is quite complex.

We know that diffusional barriers selectively retard the entrance from the bloodstream of many types of molecules into the brain. These barriers have been demonstrated for most of the suspected central synaptic agents. In addition, we suspect that extracellular catabolic enzymes could destroy the transmitter as it diffuses to the postulated site of action. A further complicating aspect of these gross methods of administration is that the interval of time from the administration of the agent to the recording of the response is usually quite long (several seconds to several minutes) in comparison with the millisecond intervals required for junctional transmission. The delay in response further reduces the likelihood of detecting the primary site of action on one of a chain of neurons.

*Microelectrophoresis*

The student will now realize how important it is to have methods of drug administration equal in sophistication to those with which the electrical phenomena are detected. The most practical micromethod of drug administration yet devised is based upon the principle of electrophoresis. Micropipettes are constructed in which one or several barrels contain an ionized solution of the chemical substance under investigation. The substance is applied by appropriately directing the current flow. The microelectrophoretic technique, when applied with controls to rule out the effects of pH, electrical current, and diffusion of the drug to neighboring neurons, has been able to overcome the major limitations of the classical neuropharmacological techniques. Frequently, a multiple-barreled electrode is constructed from which one records the spontaneous extracellular discharges of single neurons while other attached pipettes are utilized to apply drugs. One can also construct an intracellular microelectrode glued to an extracellular drug-containing multi-electrode, so that the transmembrane effects of these suspected transmitter agents can be compared with the effects of nerve pathway stimulation. The intracellular electrode can also be used to poise the relative polarization of the membrane and let us detect whether the applied suspected transmitter and that released by nerve stimulation cause the membrane to approach identical ionic equilibrium potentials.

Considerable experimentation with this technique has made possible certain generalizations regarding the actions of each putative neurotransmitter which has been studied. These substances are reviewed in detail in each of the chapters which follow. However, it should be borne in mind at the outset that certain substances have more or less invariable actions, e.g. gamma-aminobutyrate and glycine always act to inhibit, while glutamate and aspartate always excite. So far as we know, these actions arise from increased membrane conductances to Na, K, or Cl in every case. Other substances have many kinds of effects, depending upon the nature of the cell whose receptors are being tested. Thus, acetylcholine frequently excites but can also inhibit, and the receptors for either response can be nicotinic or muscarinic. Similarly, dopamine, norepinephrine, and serotonin almost always inhibit, but they have a few excitatory actions which are probably not completely artifactual.

## Pharmacology of Synaptic Effects

The fourth criterion for identification of a synaptic transmitter requires identical pharmacological effects of drugs potentiating or blocking postsynaptic responses to both the neurally released and administered samples. Because the pharmacological effects are often not identical (most "classical" blocking agents are extrapolated to brain from effects on peripheral autonomic organs), this fourth criterion is often satisfied indirectly with a series of circumstantial pieces of data. Recently, with the advent of drugs blocking the synthesis of specific transmitter agents, the pharmacology for certain families of transmitters has been improved.

The application of drugs has thus far been evaluated on four types of single-cell activity. The response of the cell to the putative transmitter agent and to the neurally released substance can be compared with respect to effects on: (a) spontaneous activity, (b) orthodromic synaptically evoked activity, (c) antidromic activity, and (d) induced effects caused by excitatory or inhibitory substances applied from another barrel of the micropipette. These techniques have been most successful when applied to large neurons, whose selected afferent pathways can be stimulated and the transmembrane effects specifically analyzed. However, when the unit recording techniques are applied to the mammalian brain, visualization and selection of the neuron under investigation are almost impossible. Although we can generally select a relatively specific brain region in which to insert the microelectrode assembly, we must utilize electrophysiological criteria for its identification. We must also depend upon geometrical attributes of the nerve cell to encounter its electrical activity as the electrode is navigated by blind mechanical means through the brain. Our ability to encounter cells in the brain depends partly on the size and

FIGURE 2-4. Ten steps in the synaptic transmission process are indicated in this idealized synaptic connection. Step 1 is transport down the axon. Step 2 is the electrically excitable membrane of the axon. Step 3 involves the organelles and enzymes present in the nerve terminal for synthesizing, storing, and releasing the transmitter, as well as for the process of active re-uptake. Step 4 includes the enzymes present in the extracellular space and within the glia for catabolizing excess transmitter released from nerve terminals. Step 5 is the postsynaptic receptor which triggers the response of the postsynaptic cell to the transmitter. Step 6 shows the organelles within the postsynaptic cells which respond to the receptor trigger. Step 7 is the interaction between genetic mechanism of the postsynaptic nerve cell and its influences on the cytoplasmic organelles which respond to transmitter action. Step 8 includes the possible "plastic" steps modifiable by events at the specialized synaptic contact zone. Step 9 includes the electrical portion of the nerve cell membrane which, in response to the various transmitters, is able to integrate the postsynaptic potentials and produce an action potential. Step 10 is the continuation of the information transmission by which this postsynaptic cell sends an action potential down its axon.

---

type of the electrode assembly we use, partly on the size and spontaneous activity of the cell we are approaching, and partly on the surgical or chemical means by which we have prepared the animal (namely, presence or absence of anesthesia, homeostatic levels of blood pressure and tissue oxygen and carbon dioxide). Even with very fine microelectrodes, the analysis does not take place in a completely undisturbed system since many connections must be broken by the physical maneuvering of the electrode. The leakage of cytoplasmic constituents, including potential transmitter agents and metabolic enzymes, can only be considered as part of the background artifact of the system.

THE STEPS OF SYNAPTIC TRANSMISSION

Let us now conclude this chapter by examining in a summary fashion the mechanisms of presumed synaptic transmission for the

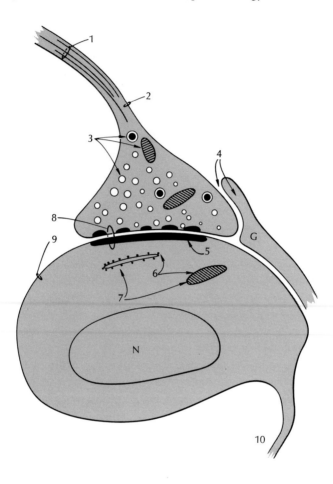

mammalian central nervous system. Each step in such transmission constitutes one of the potential sites of central drug action (Fig. 2-4). A natural or imposed stimulus activates an all-or-none action potential in an axon by depolarizing its transmembrane potential above the threshold level. The action potential propagates in an unattentuated manner to the nerve terminal where the depolarization activates a mobilization process allowing the specific transmitter for the junction to act upon the postsynaptic cell. From companion biochemical experiments (to be described in the next chapters), the transmitter substance is believed to be stored within the microvesicles or synaptic vesicles seen in nerve endings by electron microscopy. In certain types of nerve junctions, miniature postsynaptic potentials can be seen in the absence of conducted presynaptic action potentials. These miniature potentials have a quantatized effect on the postsynaptic membrane in that occasional potentials are statistical multiples of the smallest measurable potentials. The biophysical quanta have been related to the synaptic vesicles, although the proof for this relationship is still circumstantial.

When the transmitter is released from its storage site by the presynaptic action potential, the effects on the postsynaptic cells cause either excitatory or inhibitory postsynaptic potentials, depending upon the nature of the postsynaptic cell's receptor for the particular transmitter agent. If sufficient excitatory postsynaptic potentials summate temporally from various inputs onto the cell, the postsynaptic cell will integrate these potentials and give off its own all-or-nothing action potential, which is then transmitted to each of its own axon terminals, and the process continues.

SELECTED REFERENCES

Bloom, F. E. (1972). Localization of neurotransmitters by electron microscopy. *Proc. Assoc. Res. Nerv. Ment. Dis. 2*, 25.

Bodian, D. (1967). Neurons, circuits and neuroglia. In *The Neurosciences—A Study Program* (F. O. Schmitt, G. C. Quarton, and T. Melnechuk, eds.), p. 6. Rockefeller University Press, New York.

Brodie, B. B., H. Hurz, and L. S. Schanker (1960). The importance of dissociation constant and lipid solubility in influencing the passage of drugs into the cerebrospinal fluid. *J. Pharmacol. 130*, 20.

Eccles, J. C. (1964). *The Physiology of Synapses.* Academic Press, New York.

Grafstein, B. (1969). Axonal transport: communication between soma and synapse. *Advances in Biochemical Psychopharmacl. 1*, 11.

Hodgkin, A. L., and A. F. Huxley (1952). Currents carried by sodium and potassium ions through the membrane of the giant axon of Loligo. *J. Physiol. 116*, 449.

Iversen, L. L. (1971). Role of transmitters uptake mechanisms in synaptic neurotransmission. *Brit. J. Pharmacol. 41*, 571.

Katz, B. (1966). *Nerve, Muscle and Synapse.* McGraw-Hill, New York.

Lajtha, A., and D. H. Ford (1968). Brain barrier systems. *Progr. Brain. Res. 29*, 1.

Lasek, R. (1970). Protein transport in neurons. *Int. Rev. Neurobiol. 13*, 289.

Loewi, O. (1921). Uber humorale Ubertragbarkeit der Herznervenwirkung. *Pflugers Arch. ges. Physiol. 189*, 239.

Weight, F. F. (1971). Mechanisms of synaptic transmission. *Neurosciences Res. 4*, 1.

# 3 | Biochemistry of the Central Nervous System

BEFORE ENTERING into a discussion of the biochemistry of nervous tissue, it is of some importance to describe the kinds of preparations of neural tissue that have been employed in neurochemical studies as well as the techniques available for the assay of enzymes and substrates. There is no universal preparation that is satisfactory for all types of biochemical analyses. Indeed, some of our currently accepted neurochemical information derives from preparations of unknown composition that consequently contain unknown contributions of glial or Schwann cell tissue. As stated in the Introduction, the kind of preparation used can be the critical determinant of the success of a research project.

## TECHNIQUES AND PREPARATIONS

The various techniques and preparations used in neurochemical studies may be listed as follows, starting with whole animal preparations and progressing to simpler neural elements:

(a) *Arterio-venous differences.* Pioneered by Schmidt in 1928, this technique involves sampling arterial blood for $O_2$ and $CO_2$ (generally the carotid artery is used) and simultaneously measuring the concentration of these gases in venous blood leaving the brain via the jugular vein. On occasion, glucose and a variety of metabolites such as pyruvate and lactate have also been determined. From these studies it was found that the respiratory quotient is usually very close to one, indicating that carbohydrate is the primary energy source of the brain.

(b) *Brain lesions.* Using stereotactic localization, relatively discrete areas of brain tissue can be destroyed. With this technique, Harvey recently demonstrated a cholinergic mechanism for thirst by lesioning the septal area of the forebrain, and Cotman and his associates observed the development of the commissural system following entorhinal lesions.

(c) *Whole brain perfusion.* In this procedure, involving extensive and literally death-defying surgery, arterial and venous blood vessels in the head region of the cat, other than vessels that are cannulated for the perfusion, are occluded, and defibrinated blood or an artificial solution containing erythrocytes and albumin is perfused. This technique, exploited mainly by Geiger and his associates, is not widely used, not only because of the difficult operative procedure but also because of the abnormal EEG and abnormal values of glucose utilization. More recently the isolated dog brain has been used successfully by Gilboe and his associates.

(d) *Perfusion of the spinal cord.* By cannulating the vertebral canal of intact bull frogs (*Rana catesbiana*), Burgen, Angelucci, and others have developed a simple preparation of central nervous system tissue. These investigators stimulated the cord by stimulating the sciatic nerve and measured the increased efflux of a variety of neuroactive substances.

(e) *Perfusion of peripheral nervous tissue.* As discussed in Chapter 4, the bulk of our current information on the turnover of acetylcholine (ACh) in nervous tissue comes from the studies of MacIntosh and his colleagues on the perfused superior cervical ganglion of the cat. The metabolism of the perfused excised organ has also been extensively studied by Larrabee, who investigated the effects of barbiturates on oxygen consumption and more recently phospholipid turnover. Numerous investigations have utilized perfused isolated peripheral nerves such as the sciatic or the vagus in studying the effect of drugs on conduction.

(f) *Cortical cups.* Plastic rings mounted on an exposed surface of the cerebral hemispheres or cerebellum have been used to collect putative neurotransmitters. Compounds such as ACh seep into the enclosed area after electrical stimulation or the administration of drugs to the animal. The technique has been refined by Mitchell and by Pepeu.

(g) *Regional cannulae.* Developed by Feldberg, who studied effects of injected catecholamines on body temperature, cannulae with two cylinders have now been devised, one cylinder for injecting material and one for withdrawing it. Both intraventricular and intracerebral cannulae are available.

(h) *Tissue culture.* Murray and co-workers have successfully cultured a variety of neural elements, including the superior cervical ganglion and spinal neurons which have been used to test neuropharmacologic agents. More recently Sato and his colleagues followed by Nirenberg have cloned neuroblastoma cells in culture, some with choline acetylase and others with tyrosine hydroxylase activity, to indicate specific transmitters associated with a cell line.

(i) *Hand dissection.* By the use of a dissecting microscope, neuronal fragments (shorn of dendritic branches) have been isolated by Roots and Johnson, Edstrom, Hydén, and Giacobini, among others. Lowry in particular has developed techniques for handling excised nervous tissue, including the development of a quartz fiber fishpole balance that can weigh amounts of tissue as little as 0.0001 $\mu$g.

(j) *Centrifugal "dissection."* Brain fractions enriched in neuronal and glial elements have been separated by Rose using Ficoll density gradient centrifugation. This technique has been questioned because uncontaminated neuronal and glial fractions have not been reproduced in other laboratories. Norton, Sellinger, and Hamberger have developed much more satisfactory procedures.

(k) *Cerebral cortical slices.* The ease of preparing brain slices coupled with the demonstration in McIlwain's laboratory that this preparation yields a propagated action potential makes tissue slices a popular tool for many biochemical investigations. Since most of the cells are intact it is unnecessary to fortify the preparation with coenzymes or other cofactors. Cut surfaces are an advantage in that added substrates may penetrate easily but a disadvantage in that leakage of materials out of the slice will also occur.

(l) *Homogenates.* The technique of disrupting cells is an obvious prelude to the isolation of enzymes and of subcellular organelles.

(m) *Nerve ending particles and synaptic vesicles.* Developed independently by De Robertis and Whittaker, these preparations derive from a sucrose density gradient centrifugation of a crude mitochondrial fraction from brain. The centrifugation results in several distinct bands of material that can be identified by electron microscopy as myelin and membrane fragments, pinched-off nerve ending particles with attached postsynaptic membrane, and mitochondria. The nerve ending particles (sometimes called synaptosomes) may be ruptured by osmotic shock to release synaptic vesicles, the putative containers of neurotransmitters. Often overlooked in the isolation of synaptosomes is the fact that the heterogeneity of brain precludes a knowledge of just what percentage of the synaptosomes are cholinergic, noradrenergic, serotonergic, etc. In addition it is difficult to determine if the properties of these particles have changed during the isolation procedure. Finally, the degree of contamination of synaptosomes with glial cells, ribosomes, and membrane fragments that may be axonal, mitochondrial, or perikaryal makes interpretation of data somewhat difficult. Some of these contaminants have been eliminated by Cotman's isolation technique using zonal centrifugation and a sucrose-Ficoll medium.

## ASSAYS

With respect to the determination of substances of biochemical interest, neurotransmitters may be assayed quantitatively using either bioassay or chemical procedures as outlined in appropriate chapters. Substrates and enzymes are determined with a variety of physico-chemical techniques. In roughly increasing order of sensitivity, these would be manometry, colorimetry, spectrophotometry, gas-liquid chromatography, microgasometry, fluorometry, and radioactivity.

Fluorometric procedures should be singled out in particular because of their inherent specificity and sensitivity. In this regard, Lowry and his colleagues have imaginatively utilized the native and inducible fluorescence of the pyridine nucleotides as first described by Greengard. By coupling substrates and enzymes to the ultimate oxidation or reduction of pyridine nucleotides, these investigators have measured as little as $10^{-19}$ moles of substrate. By way of illustration one might consider the following coupled system:

$$\text{glucose} + \text{ATP} \xrightarrow{\text{Hexokinase}} \text{glucose-6-phosphate} + \text{ADP}$$

$$\text{glucose-6-phosphate} + \text{NADP} \xrightarrow{\text{glucose-6-phosphate dehydrogenase}} \text{6-phosphogluconate} + \text{NADPH} + \text{H}^+$$

Sum: $\text{glucose} + \text{ATP} + \text{NADP} \longrightarrow \text{6-phosphogluconate} + \text{ADP} + \text{NADPH} + \text{H}^+$

It is readily apparent that, utilizing these reactions, one can determine the concentration of glucose, ATP, or the activity of hexokinase merely by making it rate-limiting in the system and measuring NADPH either spectrophotometrically or fluorometrically, depending on the sensitivity that is required.

## NEUROCHEMICAL STUDIES

With this introduction into methodology it is now proper to ask what has been measured with respect to brain biochemistry and whether the acquired information illuminates the unique function of the brain.

One approach to this subject is to go through the litany of the Embden-Meyerhof glycolytic pathway, the tricarboxylic acid cycle, the pentose phosphate shunt, and the biosynthetic and metabolic pathways of carbohydrates, lipids, nucleic acids, and proteins. All of these enzyme systems occur in brain and have been studied in more or less detail, but qualitatively there is nothing of striking import to distinguish these enzyme activities in nervous tissue from their activity in extraneuronal tissue. For example, the synthesis of ATP from glycolysis and oxidative phosphorylation appears not to be fundamentally different in brain than in other tissues and does nothing to illuminate the brain as a specialized organ. In particular, if one recalls the diversity as well as the specificity of effects of neurotropic agents, it is difficult to see the relevance of such a universal and basic mechanism as energy production in a discussion of neuropharmacology. Unless neuropharmacological agents had a peculiar affinity for nervous tissue one would not expect to encounter such a specificity among these agents if they directly inhibited glycolysis or oxidative phosphorylation. More logically, the mechanism of action of these agents might be anticipated to lie in their ability ultimately to affect neurotransmitters. This could be primarily by displacement of the neurotransmitters or by affecting the synthesis, release, attachment to receptors, catabolism, storage, or re-uptake of transmitters, or by altering ion movement in axons.

To state the obvious, then, since the brain is an organ which transmits and stores information, it seems most profitable in discussing the biochemistry of the brain to look at enzyme systems and substrates that may contribute to this specialization. In other words, if one were asked to identify biochemically a piece of tissue as brain, what would one determine? Accepting this challenge, we can now proceed to list the types of compounds and enzyme systems which can be used to elucidate the biochemical uniqueness of brain as well as to point out profitable future lines of experimental investigations:

(A) *Compounds with demonstrated electrophysiological activity.*

(B) *Compounds and enzyme systems that either occur only in the CNS or whose concentration in the brain is extraordinarily high compared with that of other tissues.* A concentration of $> 3$ mM has been arbitrarily chosen as a cutoff point.

(C) *Compounds in which a change in concentration in brain has been shown to correlate with a change in the behavioral state of the animal.*

The composite flow sheet of Figure 3-1 covers to a large extent the listings above. The arrows are not intended to imply direct conversions but merely precursor relationships. For convenience, compounds in Group A are in capital letters; compounds in Group B are enclosed in blocks, and compounds in Group C are underlined.

The graph properly begins with glucose, because in brain, in contrast to other tissues, virtually everything except essential amino acids is derived from this substrate. For example, when labeled glucose is incubated with brain cortical slices, labeled aspartate and glutamate appear within a few minutes after the addition of the glucose to the flasks. The same occurs *in vivo* as well as in brain perfusion experiments.

The knowledge that glucose is under normal conditions the primary if not the sole substrate of the brain *in vivo* derives from two experimental findings. First, as stated earlier, in measuring A-V differences in $O_2$ and $CO_2$ in the blood going through the brain, a respiratory quotient of 1 was obtained, indicating that the oxidation of carbohydrates rather than amino acids or fatty acids is the primary source of energy. Further, when the A-V differences of glucose, glutamate, lactate, and pyruvate were determined, the only compound removed in large amounts from the arterial blood was glucose, and the only product that was released in large quantities was $CO_2$. The second line of evidence implicating glucose derives from experiments on the hypoglycemia induced either by hepatectomy or by the administration of insulin. In these experiments the fall in blood glucose correlated with a cerebral dysfunction that ranged from mild behavioral impairment to coma. This CNS effect can be completely reversed by the administration of glucose, maltose, or mannose, the latter two being converted to glucose. It is not reversed by lactate, pyruvate, or glutamate (perhaps because these agents do not penetrate the blood-brain barrier at a high enough rate). In insulin coma, with its concomitant low cerebral metabolic rate, there is enough glucose and glycogen to last about 90 minutes; then other cerebral metabolites are utilized. This calculation correlates with the observation that in insulin coma irreversible damage occurs after 90 minutes despite the subsequent administration of glucose. This irreversibility may be due to the fact that vital amino acids and lipids are utilized in an attempt to maintain cerebral metabolism.

The first step in glucose metabolism involves a phosphorylation by ATP (via the enzyme hexokinase) to form glucose-6-phosphate. About 90 per cent of this phosphate ester is metabolized through the well-known Embden-Meyerhof glycolytic pathway and about 10 per cent is oxidized via the pentose phosphate cycle. This latter system, sometimes referred to as the hexose monophosphate shunt, does not lead directly to ATP synthesis, as is the case with glycolysis or oxidative phosphorylation. Instead, it appears to function primarily in providing reduced nicotinamide adenine dinucleotide phosphate (NADPH), vital in lipid biosynthesis, and the pentose phosphates that are required in the *de novo* synthesis of nucleotides.

The Embden-Meyerhof pathway leads to triose phosphates which are involved in the synthesis of lipids. The high concentration of lipids is a unique feature of brain since about 50 per cent of the dry weight of brain is lipid compared with 6 to 20 per cent in other organs of the body. In further contrast to other tissues, there is only free cholesterol and virtually no cholesterol esters in brain.

In addition to cholesterol, brain lipids include glycerides and sphingolipids of very complex composition. The composition of some of these compounds is shown in Table 3-1. Protein-lipid complexes are also found in nervous tissue and are referred to as proteolipids or lipoproteins, depending on the physical characteristics of the molecule. Phosphatidopeptides have also been reported in the brain. Although the chemistry of brain lipids is fairly well known and much is being learned currently of the synthesis and catabolism of lipids, the function of these compounds is still unclear. What is clear is that most lipids serve as structural components, either in myelin or in membranes of the various cellular organelles, and exhibit a slow turnover. However, a metabolic function for phosphoinositides has been suggested by several investigators. Among phosphatides, the inositol phosphatides show the most rapid incorporation of $^{32}PO_4$, both *in vivo* and *in vitro;* in addition this turnover in the superior cervical ganglion is stimulated either by the addition of ACh or by preganglionic stimulation.

Although the function of the complex lipids is unknown, their implication in certain genetic types of mental retardation known as the cerebral lipidoses is well documented. Thus, for example, in Tay-Sachs disease there is an accumulation of gangliosides, in Gaucher's disease the cerebroside content of the brain rises, and in Niemann-Pick disease there is an accumulation of both sphingomyelin and gangliosides. It is also known that in demyelinating diseases the cerebroside and sphingomyelin content of the brain declines and that there is a formation of cholesterol esters.

Continuing with the scheme in Figure 3-1, the offshoot giving rise to ACh, glycine, and prostaglandins will be dealt with where these neurotransmitters, real or putative, are discussed in the subsequent chapters.

TABLE 3.1. Lipid Structures

| Basic Structure | $R_1$ | $R_2$ | X | Compound |
|---|---|---|---|---|
| $CH_2$—O—$R_1$<br>$R_2$—O—CH<br>$\quad\quad$ O<br>$\quad\quad$ ‖<br>$CH_2$—O—P—O—X<br>$\quad\quad$ O−<br><br>glycerophosphate | fatty acid | fatty acid | $CH_2CH_2NH_2$ | phosphatidylethanol-amine |
| | fatty acid | fatty acid | $CH_2CH_2N^+(CH_3)_3$ | phosphatidylcholine |
| | fatty acid | fatty acid | (inositol ring) | phosphatidylinositol (di- and triphospho-inositides have phosphate on position 4 and 5) |
| | H | $OPO_3H$ | H | cardiolipin (diphosphatidyl glycerol) |

| Basic Structure | Addition | Compound |
|---|---|---|
| $CH_3(CH_2)_{12}CH$═<br>$CH(OH)CH(NH_2)CH_2OH$<br><br>sphingosine | fatty acid | ceramide |
| | fatty acid, phosphorylcholine | sphingomyelin |
| | galactose | psychosine |
| | galactose, fatty acid | cerebroside |
| | galactose, fatty acid, sulfate | sulfatide |
| | glucose, galactose, fatty acid, N-acetylneuraminic acid, N-acetylgalactosamine | ganglioside |

$$HO_2C—\overset{\overset{O}{\|}}{C}—CH_2—CHOH—\overset{\overset{H}{|}}{\underset{\underset{O}{\underset{\|}{NH—C—CH_3}}}{C}}——(CHOH)_3—CH_2OH$$

N-acetylneuraminic acid (sialic acid)

Glutamate is the next compound we encounter in Figure 3-1 which fulfills our criteria for neuropharmacological interest. Besides its obvious utility in the brain as an energy source in coupled phosphorylation and as an amino acid for protein synthesis, glutamate has four other functions. It serves as:

1. a "detoxifying" substrate trapping $NH_3$ to form glutamine;
2. the precursor of $\gamma$-aminobutyric acid (GABA);
3. one of the amino acids in glutathione;
4. a "universal" excitatory amino acid.

The possible neurotransmitter roles of glutamate and of GABA will be discussed in Chapter 8. Also to be discussed in that chapter is the "GABA shunt," a sequence of reactions unique to brain, in which glutamate functions catalytically to produce succinate from $\alpha$-oxoglutarate without invoking $\alpha$-oxoglutarate dehydrogenase. In its role in the pathways sketched in Figure 3-1, GABA condenses with choline to form $\gamma$-aminobutyrylcholine, with arginine to yield $\gamma$-guanidinobutyrate, and with histidine to produce $\gamma$-aminobutyrylhistidine. $\gamma$-Aminobutyrylcholine and $\gamma$-guanidobutyrate have been shown to exert an inhibitory effect on evoked cortical potentials. However, the high concentrations that were necessary to evoke a response makes their physiological function suspect. Virtually nothing is known about the possible physiological role of $\gamma$-aminobutyrylhistidine.

The relationship between ammonia levels in the brain and convulsions has been demonstrated in a variety of experimental procedures. Although the cerebral origin of endogenous ammonia production is still unclear, the role of glutamate and glutamine synthetase in ammonia disposal is well established. Thus the infusion of ammonium salts into dogs results in an increased level of cerebral glutamine. Glutamine levels are presumably regulated by diffusion of the compound into the general circulation to the kidney where glutaminase would remove ammonia. The ammonia would be eliminated either as a cation or via the urea cycle. Under normal conditions glutamine might be regarded as a storehouse for glutamate; the observation that glutaminase is an allosteric enzyme

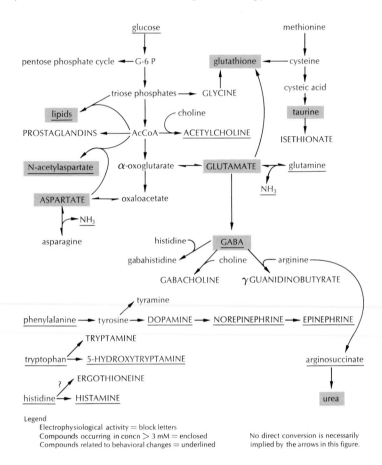

FIGURE 3-1. Various interrelationships among compounds of neuropharmacological interest.

that is activated by phosphate, ammonia, and nucleoside triphosphates and inhibited by glutamate suggests that the conversion of glutamine to glutamate is under fine metabolic control.

Glutathione is a tripeptide consisting of glutamic acid, cysteine, and glycine. Although glutathione has been known for about forty years, its function still remains elusive. It does serve as the coenzyme for the conversion of methylglyoxal to lactic acid by glyoxylase, and the isomerization of maleylacetoacetate to fumarylacetoacetate, but these reactions are not considered important enough to explain its high concentration in brain. Rather, speculation on the role of the tripeptide has always revolved around its oxidation and reduction. The oxidized or disulfide form of glutathione is rapidly reduced by a specific NADPH-dependent glutathione reductase in brain; the reaction is essentially irreversible. Glutathione may be oxidized either in maintaining other cerebral constituents in a reduced form or in its destruction of hydrogen peroxide that is formed in oxidase reactions, e.g. xanthine oxidase. This cycle would then be:

1. $R\text{-}S\text{-}S\text{-}R + 2GSH \longrightarrow 2RSH + G\text{-}S\text{-}S\text{-}G$

   or

   $H_2O_2 + 2GSH \longrightarrow 2H_2O + G\text{-}S\text{-}S\text{-}G$

2. $G\text{-}S\text{-}S\text{-}G + NADPH + H^+ \longrightarrow 2GSH + NADP^+$

The NADPH would presumably be provided by the activity of glucose-6-phosphate dehydrogenase and 6-phosphogluconate dehydrogenase in the pentose phosphate cycle.

We would not be *au courant* if we failed to describe a final neuropharmacological implication of glutamate, the Chinese restaurant syndrome. Some individuals experience painful reactions after eating Chinese food. The syndrome has been traced to the large amount of monosodium glutamate used in some recipes.

The transamination of glutamate with oxaloacetate leads to aspartate. Although in some invertebrates this amino acid serves as an organic anion reservoir, in mammalian tissue its role appears to be metabolic. Like glutamate, aspartate has central excitatory activity on iontophoretic application, can serve as a readily available energy source, and can also trap ammonia to form asparagine. Aspartic acid is a requisite in *de novo* nucleotide synthesis and in the arginosuccinic acid synthetase reaction in brain (see below).

In the presence of acetyl CoA and a specific enzyme from brain, aspartate forms N-acetylaspartate, a very intriguing compound. N-acetylaspartate is of interest in that (a) next to glutamic acid it is the amino acid or derivative in highest concentration in the brain and (b) it appears to have a primarily neuronal localization. Although in weanling animals the acetyl group can contribute to lipid biosynthesis in the brain, in adults the compound is believed to be somewhat inert metabolically. Attempts to label N-acetylaspartate by injecting radioactive precursors or *in vitro* by incubating cerebral slices with labeled glucose or aspartate have yielded only trace amounts of radioactive N-acetylaspartate. However, when labeled N-acetylaspartate is injected intracerebrally, the compound is taken up in a small rapidly turning-over pool associated with the tricarboxylic acid cycle and exhibits a half-life of about six minutes. Thus, as with other amino acids, there appear to be two pools in brain. The hydrolysis of N-acetylaspartate is catalyzed by a relatively specific enzyme designated acylase II that resides primarily in glial tissue.

The fact that endogenous N-acetylaspartate has been shown to be localized in cell cytoplasm, that it has an apparently long turnover time, and that as a dicarboxylic acid it contributes approximately 11 meq of anion/kg of brain, raises the possibility that acetylaspartate functions solely as an anion to help defray the so-called "anion deficit" that exists.

Arising from the metabolism of the essential amino acid methionine are cysteic acid and taurine. This pair is reminiscent electrophysiologically of the glutamate-GABA duo in that the first member of the pair is excitatory and the second is inhibitory. Since very little is known about either cysteic acid or taurine, their possible function is still unclear. The function of taurine in liver in conjugating with bile acids to form bile salts lends some support for the hypothesis that it has an analogous role in brain in association with cholic acid derived from cholesterol metabolism.

Isethionate (hydroxyethane sulfonic acid) is formed from taurine by oxidative deamination. Both compounds have been shown to depress drug-induced cardiac excitability; the effects of taurine

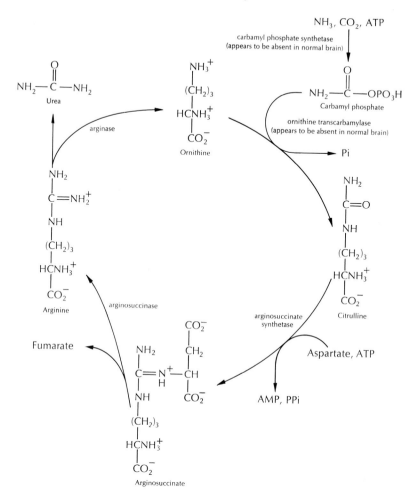

FIGURE 3-2. Urea synthesis.

are considered attributable to its conversion to isethionate. This anion has no known function in mammalian nervous tissue; in some invertebrates it serves as a principal organic anion.

A rather puzzling situation exists with respect to urea in the brain. Arginosuccinate synthetase, the arginosuccinate-splitting enzyme, and arginase have been found in the brain. However, at-

TABLE 3.2. Hereditary Diseases Associated with Cerebral Impairment

| Disorder | Defect |
|---|---|
| (A) Amino Acid Metabolism | |
| arginosuccinic aciduria | arginosuccinase |
| citrullinemia | arginosuccinic acid synthetase |
| cystathionuria | cystathionine cleaving enzyme |
| Hartnup disease | trytophan transport |
| histidinemia | histidase |
| homocystinuria | cystathionine synthetase |
| hydroxyprolinemia | hydroxyproline oxidase |
| hyperammonemia | ornithine transcarbamylase |
| hyperprolinemia | proline oxidase |
| maple syrup urine disease | valine, leucine, and isoleucine decarboxylation |
| phenylketonuria | phenylalanine hydroxylase |
| (B) Lipid Metabolism | |
| abetalipoproteinemia (acanthocytosis) | $\beta$-lipoproteins |
| cerebrotendonous xanthomatosis | cholesterol |
| Gaucher's disease | cerebrosides |
| juvenile amaurotic idiocy | gangliosides (?) |
| Krabbe's globoid dystrophy | cerebrosides |
| Kuf's disease | gangliosides (?) |

tempts to find carbamyl phosphate synthetase and ornithine trans-carbamylase have been negative. It is conceivable that citrulline is not formed from ornithine in brain but is transported there, giving rise to a modified urea cycle that is in point of fact acyclic. The indication in Figure 3-1 that a change in the level of argino-succinate in the brain is related to a behavioral change stems from findings in a rare genetic disease called arginosuccinic aciduria. In this disease, characterized by a severe mental deficiency and con-vulsions, large amounts of arginosuccinic acid are excreted in the urine; a high concentration of the compound is also found in the cerebrospinal fluid. Since urinary urea formation is within normal

TABLE 3.2. *Continued*

| Disorder | Defect |
| --- | --- |
| metachromatic leukodystrophy | sulfatides |
| Niemann-Pick disease | gangliosides and sphingomyelins |
| Refsum's disease | 3,7,11,15-tetramethylhexadecanoic acid |
| Tay-Sachs disease | gangliosides |
| (C) Carbohydrate Metabolism | |
| galactosemia | galactose-1-phosphate uridyl transferase |
| glycogen storage disease (type 2) | $\alpha$-glucosidase |
| Hurler's disease | chondroitin sulfuric acid $\beta$ |
| Umvericht myoclonus epilepsy | polysaccharides (?) |
| (D) Miscellaneous | |
| cretinism | thyroid hormone |
| Hallevorden-Spaatz disease | iron deposition in basal ganglia |
| intermittent acute porphyria | $\delta$-aminolevulinic acid |
| subacute necrotizing encephalomyelopathy | thiamine triphosphate |
| Lesch-Nyhan syndrome | hypoxanthine-guanine phosphoribosyl transferase |
| Wilson's disease | ceruloplasmin |

range, it is thought that the genetic block is not in the liver but may well be localized in the brain. The urea cycle is depicted in Figure 3-2.

Finally, to complete the outline in Figure 3-1, we turn to the three essential aromatic amino acids, phenylalanine, tryptophan, and histidine. It is interesting to look at them as a group since (a) they all are associated with congenital errors of metabolism that produce mental retardation and (b) they all give rise to neuroactive amines. In the case of tyrosine (derived from phenylalanine in the liver) and tryptophan, the metabolic pathways are strikingly similar since decarboxylation produces pressor agents (tyramine, tryptamine), whereas oxidation prior to decarboxylation yields presumptive neurotransmitters (dopamine, norepinephrine, epinephrine, and serotonin). With histidine, decarboxylation also gives rise to a vaso-active substance (histamine).

In this chapter on the biochemistry of the central nervous system no attempt has been made to discuss the two dozen or more genetic abnormalities that are associated with mental retardation; those that are noted are mentioned only because they were associated with compounds that were discussed for other reasons. Aberrant amino acid, carbohydrate, and lipid metabolism may all produce mental deficiencies. Rather than illuminating a specific reaction that is vital to normal mental development, these genetic blocks dramatically point out the necessity of totally integrated metabolism. Table 3-2 lists some genetic abnormalities that are associated with cerebral impairment.

No discussion of nucleic acids and proteins has been presented in this chapter since (a) the synthetic and catabolic pathways of these macromolecules in brain do not appear to be basically different from those in other tissues so that they do not fit into the scheme as shown in Figure 3-1 and (b) their relationship to memory and learning procedures is discussed in Chapter 10. This omission is not meant to imply that proteins of brain are identical with extraneural proteins. Several soluble proteins have been isolated which immunologically represent brain-specific protein. To date, however, no function has been ascribed to these proteins. The two most prominently studied proteins are the S-100 and the 14-3-2, the former with a glial localization, and the latter primarily neuronal. Both proteins have recently been shown to be synthesized *in vitro* by a polyribosomal preparation of rat brain.

Recently Berl and his colleagues have isolated actomyosin-like proteins from brain. This actomyosin protein, with $Mg^{++}$, $Ca^{++}$-activated ATPase activity, is called neurostenin and is composed of neurin, found in synaptosomal membranes, and stenin, found in vesicles. The obvious implication here is that neurin and stenin are involved in exocytosis by virtue of the conformational change induced by the interaction of the two proteins at the nerve terminal with subsequent release of transmitter.

The attempt in this chapter has been to explain the functional uniqueness of brain in terms of biochemistry. To this end we can point to a variety of substrates and reactions that appear to distinguish and characterize nervous tissue, but in reality we have still failed to explain the uniqueness of brain. We still cannot define the particular specialization of the brain on the basis of our current biochemical knowledge. Neither, of course, can we explain biochemically the function of other specialized organs such as the kidney. This specialization is morphological. The major biochemical contribution is the synthesis of specific macromolecules: the biochemistry of morphogenesis is really DNA → RNA → protein. Nevertheless the reactions discussed in this chapter coupled with the knowledge of neurotransmitters to be presented may be of fundamental importance in explaining the action of neuropharmacological agents.

SELECTED REFERENCES

Amano, T., E. Richelson, and M. Nirenberg (1972). Neurotransmitter synthesis by neuroblastoma clones. *Proc. Nat. Acad. Sci. U.S.A.* 69, 258.

Angelucci, L. (1956). Experiments with perfused frog's spinal cord. *Brit. J. Pharmacol. 11*, 161.

Augusti-Tocco, G., and G. Sato (1969). Establishment of functional clonal lines of neurons from mouse neuroblastoma. *Proc. Nat. Acad. Sci. U.S.A. 64*, 311.

Bartolini, A., and G. Pepeu (1967). Investigations into the acetylcholine output from the cerebral cortex of the cat in the presence of hyoscine. *Brit. J. Pharmacol. Chemotherap. 31*, 66.

Berl, S., S. Puszkin, and W. J. Wiklas (1973). Actomyosin-like protein in brain. *Science 179*, 441.

Birks, R., and F. C. MacIntosh (1961). Acetylocholine metabolism of a sympathetic ganglion. *Can. J. Biochem. Physiol. 39*, 787.

Blomstrand, C., and A. Hamberger (1970). Amino acid incorporation *in vitro* into protein of neuronal and glial cell-enriched fractions. *J. Neurochem. 17*, 1187.

Bunzl, A., A. S. V. Burgen, B. D. Burns, N. Pedley, and K. G. Terroux (1954). Methods for studying the reflex activity of the frog's spinal cord. *Brit. J. Pharmacol. 9*, 229.

DeRobertis, E., G. R. L. Arnaiz, and A. D. DeIraldi (1962). Isolation of synaptic vesicles from nerve endings of the rat brain. *Nature 194*, 794.

Drewes, L. R., and D. D. Gilboe (1973). Glycolysis and permeation of glucose and lactate in the isolated perfused dog brain during anoxia and postanoxic recovery. *J. Biol. Chem. 248*, 2489.

Edström, A. (1964). The ribonucleic acid in the Mauthner neuron of the goldfish. *J. Neurochem. 11*, 309.

Eichberg, J., Jr., V. P. Whittaker, and R. M. C. Dawson (1964). Distribution of lipids in subcellular particles of guinea pig brain. *Biochem. J. 92*, 91.

Feldberg, W., and V. J. Lotti (1967). Temperature responses to mono-amines and an inhibition of MAO injected into the cerebral ven-tricals of rats. *Brit. J. Pharmacol. Chemotherap.* *31*, 152.

Gaitonde, M. K., S. A. Marchi, and D. Richter (1964). The utilization of glucose in the brain and other organs of the cat. *Proc. Roy. Soc. B.* *160*, 124.

Geiger, A. (1958). Correlation of brain metabolism and function by the use of a brain perfusion method *in situ*. *Physiol. Rev.* *38*, 1.

Giacobini, E. (1965). Metabolism and function studied in single neu-rons. *Ann. 1st. Super, Sanita.* *1*, 500.

Hyden, H. (1960). *The Cell* (J. Brachet and A. E. Mirsky, eds.), Vol. 4, Academic Press, New York.

Jacobsen, J. G., and L. H. Smith, Jr. (1968). Biochemistry and physi-ology of taurine and taurine derivatives. *Physiol. Rev.* *48*, 424.

Kety, S., and C. F. Schmidt (1948). The nitrous oxide method for the quantitative determination of cerebral blood flow in man: theory, procedure and normal values. *J. Clin. Invest.* *27*, 476.

Kohl, H. H., and O. Z. Sellinger (1972). Protein synthesis in neuronal perikarya isolated from cerebral cortex of the immature rat. *J. Neurochem.* *19*, 699.

Lowry, O. H., J. V. Passonneau, D. W. Schulz, and M. K. Rock (1961). The measurement of pyridine nucleotides by enzymatic cycling. *J. Biol. Chem.* *236*, 2746.

Lynch, G. S., S. Mosko, T. Parks, and C. W. Cotman (1973). Reloca-tion and hyperdevelopment of the dentate gyrus commissural sys-tem after entorhinal lesions in immature rats. *Brain Res.* *50*, 174.

McIlwain, H., and R. Rodnight (1962). *Practical Neurochemistry*, Little, Brown, Boston.

McIlwain, H., and H. S. Bachelard (1971). *Biochemistry and the Cen-tral Nervous System*, Churchill, London.

Matschinsky, P. M., J. V. Passonneau, and O. H. Lowry (1968). Quan-titative histochemical analysis of glycolytic intermediates and co-factors with an oil well technique. *J. Histochem. Cytochem.* *16*, 29.

Matsuura, S., S. Kawaguchi, M. Ichiki, M. Sorimachi, K. Kataoka, and A. Inouye (1969). Perfusion of frog's spinal cord as a convenient method for neuropharmacological studies. *Europ. J. Pharmacol.* *6*, 13.

Mitchell, J. F. (1963). The spontaneous and evoked release of acetyl-choline from the cerebral cortex. *J. Physiol.* (Lond.) *165*, 98.

Murray, M. R. (1965). *Cells and Tissues in Culture* (E. W. Willmer, ed.), Vol. 2, Academic Press, New York.

Nadler, J. V., and J. R. Cooper (1972). Metabolism of the aspartyl moiety of N-acetyl-L-aspartic acid in the rat brain. *J. Neurochem.* *19*, 2091.

Norton, W. T., and S. E. Podluso (1970). Neuronal soma and whole neuroglia of rat brain: a new isolation technique. *Science 167*, 1144.

Ratner, S., H. Morell, and E. Carvalho (1960). Enzymes of arginine metabolism in brain. *Arch. Biochem. Biophys. 91*, 280.

Roots, B. I., and P. V. Johnson (1967). Neurons of ox brain nuclei: their isolation and appearance by light and electron microscopy. *J. Ultrastruct. Res. 10*, 350.

Rose, S. P. R. (1965). Preparation of enriched fraction from cerebral cortex containing isolated, metabolically active neuronal cells. *Nature 206*, 621.

Sorensen, J. P., and J. A. Harvey (1971). Decreased brain acetylcholine after septal lesions in rats: correlation with thirst. *Physiol. and Behavior 6*, 723.

Whittaker, V. P., J. A. Michaelson, and R. J. Kirkland (1964). The separation of synaptic vesicles from nerve endings particles (synaptosomes). *Biochem. J. 90*, 293.

Zomzely-Neurath, C., C. York, and B. W. Moore (1973). *In vitro* synthesis of two brain specific proteins (S-100 and 14-3-2) by polyribosomes from rat brain. *Arch. Biochem. Biophys. 155*, 58.

# 4 | Acetylcholine

THE NEUROPHYSIOLOGICAL activity of acetylcholine (ACh) has been known since the turn of the century and its neurotransmitter role since the mid-1920's. With this history it is not surprising that the graduate student or medical student assumes that everything is known about this subject. This chapter makes clear that almost the only thing definitely known in any detail about ACh is its structural formula; this is presented below:

$$(CH_3)_3N^+-CH_2CH_2-O-\overset{\displaystyle O}{\overset{\displaystyle \|}{C}}-CH_3$$
Acetylcholine

## ASSAY PROCEDURES

ACh may be assayed by its effect on biological test systems or by physico-chemical methods. Bioassay preparations include the frog rectus abdominis, the dorsal muscle of the leech, the guinea pig ileum, the rat (or cat) blood pressure, and the heart of Venus mercenaria. In general bioassays tend to be laborious, subject to interference by naturally occurring substances, and on occasion to behave in a mysterious fashion (for example, the frog rectus abdominis is not as sensitive to ACh in the summer months as in the winter, and it is not unusual to encounter a guinea pig ileum that will not respond to ACh). Nevertheless, bioassays at the present time represent one of the most sensitive ($< 1$ ng) and, under properly controlled conditions, the most specific procedure for determining ACh. It is probably true to state that the neurochemically oriented investigator's natural fear and distrust of a bioassay have hampered progress in elucidating biochemical and biophysical aspects of ACh. This statement is supported by a consideration of the recent explosion of information on norepinephrine. This neurotransmitter can also be bioassayed, but it was only after the development of sensitive fluorometric and radiometric procedures for determining components of the adrenergic nervous system that the information explosion occurred.

Until about 1965 physico-chemical methods for determining ACh were so insensitive as to be virtually useless in measuring endogenous levels of ACh. However, since then there have been reports published on enzymatic, fluorometric, and gas chromatographic techniques that in theory approach the sensitivity and specificity of the bioassays. In particular, the gas chromatographic procedure of Jenden has recently been coupled to mass spectroscopy to yield a high degree of sensitivity and specificity. Unfortunately, the cost of the apparatus limits the use of this procedure to wealthy investigators.

Recently, Goldberg and McCaman have modified a radiometric procedure devised by Reid *et al.* to yield a method for measuring ACh that will probably supplant most existing procedures. The principle of the method is that ACh is first hydrolyzed to acetate and choline by cholinesterase, and choline is phosphorylated by choline kinase with $AT^{32}P$, to produce choline-$^{32}P$-phosphate. The mixture is then put through a small column containing an anionic resin whereby $AT^{32}P$ remains on the column and the labeled choline phosphate passes through and is collected into scintillation vials for a subsequent determination of the radioactivity. With this procedure, one can determine 5 *p*moles ($5 \times 10^{-12}$ moles) of ACh.

SYNTHESIS

Acetylcholine is synthesized in a reaction catalyzed by choline acetyltransferase (choline acetylase):

$$\text{acetyl CoA} + \text{choline} \longrightarrow \text{ACh} + \text{CoA}$$

The reaction may be followed by:
1. Incubating acetyl CoA and choline and measuring ACh production by one of the methods mentioned above. An

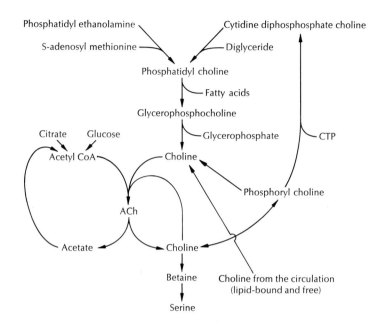

FIGURE 4-1. Acetylcholine metabolism.

anticholinesterase is usually added to inhibit hydrolysis of the ACh that is formed. Rather than adding acetyl CoA, a number of investigators generate this compound with acetyl phosphate, phosphotransacetylase, and CoA, or alternatively, acetate, ATP, CoA, and acetate thiokinase (acetate activating enzyme, acetyl CoA synthetase).

2. Incubating acetyl-$^{14}$C-CoA and choline and measuring radioactive ACh after its isolation either by precipitation as an insoluble salt such as the Reineckate or by ion exchange chromatography.

Before entering into a discussion of choline acetylase, we should take note of Figure 4-1, which depicts the possible sources of acetyl CoA and choline. In theory, the acetyl CoA for ACh synthesis may arise from glucose, through glycolysis and the pyruvate oxidase system; from citrate, either by a reversal of the condensing enzyme (citrate synthetase) or by the citrate cleavage enzyme; or from acetate through acetatethiokinase. In brain slices, homogenates, acetone powder extracts, and preparations of nerve ending particles, glucose or citrate proved to be the best sources for ACh synthesis, with acetate rarely showing any activity. However, these systems are all *in vitro* and do not necessarily reflect the situation *in vivo*. Regardless of its source, acetyl CoA is primarily synthesized in mitochondria. Since, as detailed below, choline acetyltransferase appears to be in the synaptosomal cytoplasm, another still unsolved problem is how acetyl CoA is transported out of the mitochondria to participate in ACh synthesis.

Recent evidence suggests that, in contrast to the liver, choline cannot be synthesized *de novo* in brain by successive methylations of ethanolamine. It is transported to the brain both free and in phospholipid form (possibly phosphatidyl choline) by the blood. Following the hydrolysis of ACh, about 35 to 50 per cent of the liberated choline is transported back into the presynaptic terminal by a sodium-dependent, high affinity active transport system, to be reutilized in ACh synthesis. As outlined in Figure 4-1, the remaining choline may be catabolized or alternatively become incorporated into phospholipids which can serve as a source of choline. It should be noted that lesioning in the CNS or denervation in the superior cervical ganglion produces a decrease in choline content. A curious recent observation is that when brain cortical slices are incubated for two hours in a Krebs-Ringer medium, choline accumulates to a level about ten times its original concentration. Similarly, a rapid postmortem increase in choline has been observed. The precise source of this choline is unknown.

From experiments in the superior cervical ganglia, the phrenic nerve-diaphragm, and the corneal epithelium, choline appears to be the rate-limiting factor in ACh synthesis. That is, in all these preparations, the addition of choline produced an increased synthesis of ACh.

With respect to the cellular localization of choline acetyltransferase, the highest activity is found in the caudate nucleus, retina, corneal epithelium, and central spinal roots (3000 to 4000 $\mu$g ACh synthesized/g/hr). In contrast dorsal spinal roots contain only trace amounts of the enzyme, as does the cerebellum.

Intracellularly, after differential centrifugation in a sucrose medium, choline acetyltransferase is found in mammalian brain predominantly in the crude mitochondrial fraction. This fraction contains mitochondria, nerve ending particles (synaptosomes) with enclosed synaptic vesicles, and membrane fragments. When this fraction is subjected to sucrose density gradient centrifugation, the bulk of the choline acetyltransferase is found to be associated with nerve ending particles. When these synaptosomes are ruptured by hypo-osmotic shock, synaptosomal cytoplasm can be separated from synaptic vesicles. In a solution of low ionic strength the choline acetyltransferase is adsorbed to the vesicles, but in the presence of salts at physiological concentration the enzyme is solubilized and remains in the cytoplasm. *In vivo* the enzyme is most likely present in the cytoplasm of the nerve ending particle and not in vesicles.

A cell-free system of choline acetyltransferase was first described by Nachmansohn and Machado in 1943. Since that time the enzyme from squid head ganglia, human placenta, and brain has been partially purified and some of its characteristics have been defined. As partially purified from rat brain, choline acetyltransferase has a molecular weight of about 65,000, with an apparent Michaelis constant (Km) for choline of $7.5 \times 10^{-4}$ M and for acetyl CoA of $1.0 \times 10^{-5}$ M. Currently a controversy exists on the extent of the reversibility of the reaction. The enzyme is activated by salts and is inhibited by sulfhydryl reagents. A variety of studies on the substrate specificity of the enzyme indicates that various acyl derivatives both of CoA and of ethanolamine can be utilized by the enzyme. The major gap in our knowledge of choline acetyltransferase is that as yet we do not know of any useful (i.e. potent and specific) direct inhibitor of the enzyme. Styrylpyridine derivatives inhibit the enzyme but suffer from the fact that they are light-sensitive, somewhat insoluble, and possess varying degrees of anticholinesterase activity. Hemicholinium (HC-3) inhibits the synthesis of ACh, but indirectly, by preventing the transport of choline across cell membranes.

HYDROLYSIS

The splitting of ACh into choline and acetic acid may be followed:

1. gasometrically by using a bicarbonate buffer and measuring the evolution of $CO_2$;
2. by a change in pH recorded either potentiometrically or by a color change in an indicator;
3. by using acetylthiocholine as substrate and measuring the formation of thiocholine colorimetrically with dithiobisnitrobenzoate;
4. by measuring the amount of ACh remaining after incubation.
5. by incubating ACh labeled in either the acetyl or choline moiety and isolating the labeled portion with ion-exchange chromatography.

Everybody agrees that ACh is hydrolyzed by cholinesterases but nobody is sure just how many cholinesterases exist in the body. All cholinesterases will hydrolyze not only ACh but other esters. Conversely, hydrolytic enzymes such as arylesterases, trypsin, and chymotrypsin will not hydrolyze choline esters. The problem in deciding the number of cholinesterases that exist is that different species and organs sometimes exhibit maximal activity with different substrates. For our purposes we will divide the enzymes into two rigidly defined classes: acetylcholinesterase (also called "true" or specific cholinesterase) and butyrocholinesterase (also called "pseudo" or nonspecific cholinesterase; the term "propionocholinesterase" is sometimes used since in some tissues propionylcholine is hydrolyzed more rapidly than butyrylcholine). When distinguishing between the two types of cholinesterases at least two critera should be used because of the aforementioned species or organ variation.

The first criterion is the optimum substrate. Acetylcholinesterase hydrolyzes ACh faster than butyrylcholine, propionylcholine, or tributyrin; the reverse is true with butyrocholinesterase. In addition, acetyl-$\beta$-methyl choline (methachol) is only split by acetylcholinesterase. That this criterion for distinguishing between the two esterases is not inviolate and must be used along with other indices is illustrated by the fact that the chicken brain acetylcholinesterase will hydrolyze acetyl-$\beta$-methyl choline but will also hydrolyze propionylcholine faster than ACh. Also the bee head enzyme will not hydrolyze either ACh or butyrylcholine but will split acetyl-$\beta$-methyl choline.

A second criterion that is used in differentiating the cholinesterases is the substrate concentration verus activity relationship. Acetylcholinesterase is inhibited by high concentrations of ACh so that a bell-shaped substrate concentration curve results. This is observed also when butyrylcholine or propionylcholine is used. In contrast, butyrocholinesterase is not inhibited by high substrate concentrations so that the usual Michaelis-Menten type of substrate concentration curve is obtained. The reason for this difference is that in acetylcholinesterase there is at least a two-point attachment of substrate to enzyme whereas with butyrocholinesterase the substrate is attached at only one site.

The type of cholinesterase found in a tissue is often a reflection of the tissue. This fact is used as a discriminating index between cholinesterases. In general, neural tissue contains acetylcholinesterase while nonneural tissue usually contains butyrocholinesterase. However, this is a generalization, and some neural tissue (e.g. autonomic ganglia) contains both esterases as do some extraneural organs, e.g. liver, lung. In the blood, erythrocytes contain only acetylcholinesterase while plasma contains butyrocholinesterase, but plasma has primary substrates varying from species to species. Because of its ubiquity, cholinesterase activity cannot be used as an indicator of a cholinergic system in the absence of additional supporting evidence.

A final criterion that may be applied to differentiate between the esterases is their susceptibility to inhibitors. Thus the organophosphorus anticholinesterases such as diisopropyl phosphorofluoridate (DFP) are more potent inhibitors of butyrocholinesterase whereas a compound such as WIN8077 (Ambinonium) is about two thousand times better an inhibitor of acetylcholinesterase.

In discussing the various techniques that are used to classify the cholinesterases, we touched on some aspects of the molecular properties of the enzymes. Since very little work has been done on butyrocholinesterase and since no physiological role for this enzyme (or enzymes) has been demonstrated, we will focus our attention on acetylcholinesterase. In sucrose homogenates of mammalian brain, subjected to differential centrifugation, acetylcholinesterase is found both in the mitochondrial and microsomal fractions. The latter, consisting of endoplasmic reticulum and plasma cell membranes, exhibits a higher specific activity. This localization of the enzyme is supported by electron microscopic and histochemical studies which fix the activity at membranes of all kinds both in the CNS and the peripheral nervous system.

Acetylcholinesterase has been crystallized from *Electrophorus electricus*, is electrophoretically homogeneous (crystalline enzymes are not necessarily pure), and has a molecular weight of 260,000. The most recent preparation, purified by affinity chromatography, hydrolyzed 960 mmoles of ACh/mg protein/hr thus placing it among the enzymes having the highest turnover number that is known. Recently acetylcholinesterase has been prepared from brain to almost the same degree of purity. With respect to the topography of the enzyme the twin-hatted diagram of the anionic and esteratic sites has been reproduced countless times and need not be presented again here. However, some discussion is in order since this was the first enzyme to be dissected at a molecular level. For this initiation into molecular biology we owe a debt of gratitude to Nachmansohn and his colleagues, particularly Wilson. The active center of acetylcholinesterase has two main subsites. The first is an anionic site which attracts the positive charge in ACh and the second, about 5Å distant, is an esteratic site which binds the carbonyl carbon atom of ACh. Current information suggests that the anionic site contains at least one carboxyl group, possibly from glutamate, and the esteratic site involves a histidine residue adjacent to serine. The over-all reaction is written as follows:

$$E + ACh \longrightarrow E \cdot ACh \xrightarrow{\phantom{xx}H_2O\phantom{xx}} E \cdot \underset{choline}{Acetyl} \longrightarrow E + acetic\ acid$$

Information on the architecture of the active center has been derived not only from kinetic studies using model compounds but from a group of inhibitors known as the anticholinesterases. (The pharmacology of these agents will be discussed in the last section of the chapter.) The anticholinesterases are classified as reversible and irreversible inhibitors of the enzyme. Like ACh, both types of inhibitor acylate the enzyme at the esteratic site. However, in contrast to ACh or to a reversible inhibitor such as physostigmine, the irreversible inhibitors, which are organo-phosphorus compounds, irreversibly phosphorylate the esteratic site. This phosphorylation has been shown to occur on the hydroxyl group of serine when DFP was incubated with purified acetylcholinesterase. It is interesting to note that when trypsin or chymotrypsin is treated with DFP it is also the serine hydroxyl in these proteins that is phosphorylated. Since in solution serine does not react with DFP it has been suggested that in peptide linkage serine (a) is in an oxazoline ring structure which is then susceptible to phosphorylation or (b) that amino acids, such as histidine, which surround serine promote high reactivity in the serine hydroxyl. Although the organo-phosphorus agents (referred to as nerve gases though they are actually oils) are classed as irreversible anticholinesterases, there is a slow detachment of the compounds from the enzyme. Wilson observed that hydroxylamine speeded up this dissociation and regenerated active enzyme. He then set about designing a nucleophilic agent with a spatial structure that would fit the active center of acetylcholinesterase, and did in fact produce a compound which is very active in displacing the inhibitor. This is 2-pyridine aldoxime methiodide (PAM), which has been used with moderate success in treating poisoning from organo-phosphorus compounds used as insecticides. PAM, with its quaternary ammonium group, does not penetrate the blood-brain barrier well enough to overcome central actions of the anticholinesterase. For this reason atropine is usually used as an antidote along with PAM. It will be recalled that atropine blocks the effect of ACh at neuro-effector sites and has nothing to do with acetylcholinesterase.

## THE GENESIS OF THE CHOLINERGIC TRIAD IN NEURONS

It has already been pointed out that choline acetyltransferase is found in the cytoplasm of nerve ending particles, that acetylcholinesterase is associated with cell membranes of all kinds (synaptosomal, axonal, and glial), and that ACh is localized to some extent in synaptic vesicles. It is now pertinent to inquire how these three components of the cholinergic system arrived at their respective residences.

The phenomenon of axoplasmic flow has been described in Chapter 2. This is the process by which material synthesized in the cell body moves down the axons of the peripheral nerves by mechanisms as yet not understood. In the case of choline acetyltransferase a variety of investigators have by ligation and sectioning of peripheral nerves shown that this enzyme originates in the perikaryon and travels down to the nerve terminal. With acetylcholinesterase the situation is still not clear. Again, by sectioning experiments and by the use of irreversible anticholinesterases, it has been demonstrated that the enzyme can be formed in the cell body and then move down an axon, possibly attached to neurotubules as a carrier. On the other hand, local synthesis of the enzyme in axons has also been reported. The latter results are slightly tainted by Schwann cell contamination of the neuronal preparation so that it cannot be stated with certainty whether the enzyme is synthesized by neuronal elements alone. Nevertheless, regardless of the possible contribution of satellite cells to axonal synthesis of acetylcholinesterase, it is clear that the enzyme primarily originates in the cell body. It should be kept in mind that these studies, both with choline acetyltransferase and acetylcholinesterase, were done in peripheral nerves. In fact as we explore the problem of ACh it will be apparent that for obvious technical reasons much of our information comes from experiments on the peripheral nervous system. The question is how applicable are the results of these investigations to the cholinergic neurons in the central nervous system? In the case of choline acetyltransferase and acetylcholinesterase we do not know if translocations of the enzymes occur in the CNS.

Since choline acetyltransferase is found both in cell bodies and terminals, it is understandable that ACh is localized in these two regions and that some transmitter appears within cholinergic axons. At the nerve terminal, about half the ACh is found in synaptic vesicles and half in the synaptosomal cytoplasm. In the cholinergic vesicles of the bovine superior cervical ganglion, the concentration of ACh/vesicle is about 1600 molecules; in the Torpedo vesicular population, it is about 66,000 molecules/vesicle.

How synaptic vesicles are formed and why they cluster at this location are not understood (cf. Chapter 2).

UPTAKE, STORAGE, AND RELEASE OF ACh

*Superior Cervical Ganglion*

To date the only major and thorough study of ACh turnover in nervous tissue was done originally by MacIntosh, Birks, and colleagues, and more recently by Collier using the superior cervical ganglion of the cat. By using one ganglion to assay the resting level of ACh and by perfusing the contralateral organ these investigators have determined the amount of transmitter synthesized and released under a variety of experimental conditions including electrical stimulation, the addition of an anticholinesterase to the perfusion fluid, and perfusion medium of varying ionic composition. Their results may be summarized as follows:

a. During stimulation, ACh turns over at a rate of 8 to 10

per cent of its resting content every minute, i.e. about 24 to 30 ng/min. At rest the turnover rate is about 0.5 ng/min. Since there is no change in the ACh content of the ganglion during stimulation at physiological frequencies it is evident that electrical stimulation not only releases the transmitter but also stimulates its synthesis.

b. Choline is the rate-limiting factor in the synthesis of ACh.

c. In the perfused ganglion, $Na^+$ is necessary for optimum synthesis and storage, and $Ca^{++}$ is necessary for the release of the neurotransmitter.

d. Newly synthesized ACh appears to be more readily released on nerve stimulation than depot or stored ACh.

e. About half of the choline produced by cholinesterase activity is reutilized to make new ACh.

f. At least three separate stores of ACh in the ganglion are inferred from these studies: "surplus" ACh, considered to be intracellular, which accumulates only in an eserine-treated ganglion and which is not released by nerve stimulation but is released by $K^+$ depolarization; "depot" ACh, which is released by nerve impulses and accounts for about 85 per cent of the original store; and "stationary" ACh, which constitutes the remaining 15 per cent that is non-released.

As stated above, this work on the superior cervical ganglion represents the most complete information on the turnover of ACh in the nervous system.

## Brain Slices, Nerve Ending Particles, and Synaptic Vesicles

About thirty-five years ago Mann, Tennenbaum, and Quastel demonstrated the synthesis and release of ACh in cerebral cortical slices. In the succeeding thirty-five years these observations have been repeatedly confirmed but only moderately extended. The major finding of interest in all these studies is that in the usual incubation medium the level of ACh in the slices reaches a limit and cannot be raised. In a high $K^+$ medium the total ACh is increased substantially because much of it leaks into the medium from the slices. The experiments suggest that the intracellular concentration of the neurotransmitter regulates its rate of synthesis. This concept of a negative feedback mechanism is supported by the findings that the administration of drugs such as morphine, oxotremorine, or anticholinesterases only succeed in, at the most, a doubling of the original level of ACh in the brain. Regardless of the dose of the drug, no higher level can be obtained.

The techniques of Whittaker and of De Robertis in isolating nerve ending particles with enclosed synaptic vesicles from brain have provided some new though still inconclusive data on ACh. The drawback of this technique, namely, the inhomogeneity of the brain, has already been mentioned in Chapter 3.

With the discovery of these presynaptically localized vesicles that contained ACh the conclusion was almost unavoidable that these organelles were the source of the quantal release of transmitter as described in the neurophysiological experiments of Katz and his collaborators. Thus, the obvious interpretation has been that as the nerve is depolarized, vesicles in apposition to the terminal fuse with the presynaptic membrane and ACh is released into the synaptic cleft to interact with receptors on the post-synaptic cell and to change ion permeability. The subsequent sequence of events is not clearly pictured but in some fashion, presynaptic membrane is recaptured, vesicles are resynthesized, and simultaneously or subsequently repleted with ACh; the neuron is then ready for the next quantal release of transmitter.

The electrophysiological experiments of Katz have been repeated in other laboratories and the concept of packets of ACh being discharged has been unanimously accepted. The exocytotic process has also been accepted as applied to hormonal release, e.g. pancreas, adrenal medulla. What is not yet available, however, is substantive proof that vesicles and exocytosis are involved in the release of neurotransmitters. Several years ago when investigators began to look intensively at vesicle populations in nerve preparations (usually superior cervical ganglia or neuromuscular junctions) that were stimulated under physiological conditions, no differences were noted in the number, the location, or the size of vesicles compared with unstimulated preparations. However, in recent years the electron microscopists have become more brutal in their treatment of nerve preparations and a number of papers have appeared showing vesicle depletion. In addition, coated vesicles, and vesicles that have incorporated horseradish peroxidase (both phenomena suggestive of an opening of the vesicular membrane to the medium and subsequent resealing; i.e. exocytosis), have been reported although the frequency of occurrence of these phenomena is not often stated. In these experiments the investigators have subjected the preparation, usually in the absence of choline and glucose, to prolonged electrical stimulation at high frequency or to the addition of lanthanum, black widow spider venom, or hemicholinium-3. Under these conditions one can show a depletion of ACh and a depletion of vesicular stores. However, electron micrographs of these preparations generally depict a rather frayed and moth-eaten presynaptic terminal so that the physiological significance of these experiments is questionable. It is conceivable that the absence of choline may cause a depletion of phospholipid choline from both vesicular and axolemmal membranes, thus producing this moribund appearance. The absence of an energy source may also damage the preparation. To reiterate what was stated previously, at the present time *under normal physiological conditions*, one can demonstrate release of ACh without any indication linking vesicle discharge and turnover to this release. Although at first thought one might expect to find the mechanism of transmitter release to be similar to hormonal release, the turnover of transmitter is several orders of magnitude faster than that of a hormone, and it might be predicted that vesicular reformation and repletion with transmitter could not be fast enough to keep up with the demand.

In addition to the morphological experiments cited above, other evidence that tentatively tends to support a storage role of vesicles rather than an immediate source of ACh is listed below:

1. In experiments in the phrenic nerve-diaphragm and superior cervical ganglion it has been shown that on electrical stimulation

newly synthesized ACh is released before ACh that is in a bound form; i.e. preformed store.

2. Choline acetyltransferase is localized in the cytoplasm of nerve-ending particles and not in synaptic vesicles as originally believed. Thus ACh synthesized in the synaptosomal cytoplasm has to be transported into vesicles. The demonstration of this transport using isolated vesicles is still a matter of debate with most investigators admitting failure.

3. As determined from protein turnover studies of vesicle membranes, the half-life of synaptic vesicles is calculated to be about 19 days. In addition, from disc gel electrophoretic analysis it appears that proteins of vesicle membranes are different than those of synaptosomal membranes thus arguing against a reformation of vesicles from axolemmal membrane.

In summary then, current morphological and neurochemical evidence does not support the exocytotic concept of transmitter release at nerve endings. However it should be apparent that the evidence cited above is far from unequivocal, and logical explanations can be advanced to counteract each point. Therefore, rather than invoking some gating mechanism at the terminal to explain the release of ACh in packets, it would be prudent to delay a final assessment of the function of synaptic vesicles until further information is available.

## ACTIONS OF ACh

In addition to being a neurotransmitter at certain synapses ACh also has an action on membranes that is still not understood with respect to its physiological importance. The neurotransmitter function in terms of sites can be discussed under the headings "proven," "likely," and "possible."

### Transmitter

Virtually all the criteria discussed in Chapter 2 for identifying a neurotransmitter are fulfilled by ACh at the neuromuscular junction, in autonomic ganglia, and at postganglionic parasympathetic nerve endings. In addition, in the CNS the motoneuron collaterals to the Renshaw cells have been shown to be cholinergic. Although technically difficult to establish conclusively, it is, in fact, more than *likely* that other synapses in the central nervous system are also cholinergic. A variety of histochemical and biochemical studies indicate that the hippocampus receives a cholinergic input from the medial septal nucleus and the nucleus of the diagonal band. If this cholinergic input is destroyed by placement of a lesion in the medial septal area, a decrease in endogenous ACh, choline, choline acetylase activity, and choline uptake occurs. In addition, evidence suggests that the ascending reticular arousal system and primary afferent fibers for the auditory and visual systems are also cholinergic.

With the technique of iontophoresis the following sites have been shown to be affected by ACh: caudate nucleus, ventral basal thalamus, lateral geniculate body, the supraoptic nucleus and posteromedial parts of the thalamus, cochlear nucleus, brain stem, and pyramidal cells of the cortex. In support of cholinergic junctions in the central nervous system may be offered the observation of the marked central effects of the anticholinesterases which can penetrate the blood-brain barrier, and of cholinolytic agents such as atropine. With respect to a *possible* neurotransmitter function of ACh there are a few bits of information that suggest that ACh may participate in pain reception. Thus the findings that nettles (*Urtica urens*) contain ACh and histamine, that high concentrations of ACh injected into the brachial artery of humans have been shown to result in intense pain, and that ACh applied to a blister produced a brief but severe pain, all indicate a relationship between ACh and pain. Further, when hemicholinium is instilled in a rabbit eye, the animal loses its corneal reflex concurrently as the ACh content of the corneal epithelium falls and the reflex returns when the ACh level rises to normal values. In addition, local denervation of the rabbit cornea results in a loss of 94 per cent of the ACh content of the tissue ten days after denervation. In should be noted that bradykinin and substance P produce painful reactions when applied at much lower concentrations than is necessary with ACh. That ACh may act as a sensory transmitter in thermal receptors, taste fiber endings, and chemoreceptors has also been suggested, based on the excitatory activity of the compound on these sensory nerve endings. Recently, Kravitz has found a cholinergic sensory neuron in the muscle receptor organ of the lobster.

## Membrane Effects

A variety of actions of ACh that may be viewed as membrane effects rather than neurotransmitter activity has been described and is listed below:

1. Stimulation of incorporation of inorganic phosphate into phospholipids: A number of investigators have shown that ACh at a concentration of about $10^{-4}$ M will stimulate the incorporation of $^{32}P_i$ into phospholipids, particularly phosphatidyl inositol, and phosphatidic acid. This stimulation has been demonstrated not only in salt gland, sympathetic ganglia, and brain slices but also in brain homogenates. The mechanism of this stimulation has not been rigorously proven but the current evidence suggests that ACh is stimulating the hydrolysis of phosphoinositides in synaptosomes to form membrane-bound diglyceride. It is assumed that the membrane-bound diglyceride is rate limiting in the synthesis of both phosphatidic acid and phosphoinositides.

2. Release of thiamine: Itokawa and Cooper have shown that ACh, as well as a variety of neuroactive drugs, will release thiamine from perfused nerve preparations. This releasing effect can also be demonstrated with membrane preparations from brain, spinal cord, and sciatic nerve, although with this subcellular fraction higher concentrations of ACh are necessary ($10^{-4}$ M in contrast to $10^{-6}$ M with intact preparations).

3. Release of catecholamines: It has been known for many

years that ACh releases catecholamines from chromaffin cells.

4. Conduction: That ACh is involved in the conduction process in axons has been espoused by Nachmansohn for over a quarter of a century. Both his theory and a detailed indictment of it by Koelle can be appraised in the references given at the end of this chapter. Although the evidence against the participation of ACh in conduction is overwhelming, nevertheless no satisfactory explanation has yet been given for the ability of ACh (albeit in high concentrations) to depolarize an axon.

5. Non-nervous tissue: Ciliary movement in the gill plates of *Mytilus edulis* has been observed to be under the control of ACh. Ciliary activity is increased by eserine and inhibited by atropine and *d*-tubocurarine. Ciliary motility of respiratory and esophageal tracts in mammals also appears to be controlled by ACh.

The depolarizing effect of ACh on intestinal smooth muscle has been shown to be independent of nervous intervention: this action is a direct one on smooth muscle fibers. Similarly, the hyperpolarizing action of ACh on atrial muscle in the absence of nervous control has been demonstrated. ACh has been shown to induce sporulation in the fungus *Trichoderma* and to mimic red light in photomorphogenesis in some plants.

These situations describe an activity of ACh that is independent of innervation. There is also a variety of tissues and organisms, such as human placenta, *Lactobacillus plantarum* and *Trypanosoma rhodesience*, and a fungus (*Claviceps purpurea*) in which ACh is found but where nothing is known of its action.

THE CHOLINERGIC RECEPTOR

Every few years someone states that the cholinergic receptor is in fact acetylcholinesterase. That this belief is erroneous may be construed from the following facts:

1. In the isolated electroplax of *Electrophorus electricus* the

apparent dissociation constant of the ACh-receptor complex is $5 \times 10^{-6}$ M, whereas the Michaelis constant ($K_m$) of acetylcholinesterase in this preparation is $1 \times 10^{-4}$ M.

2. Incubation of an electroplax with either $p$-chloromercuribenzoate or dithiothreitol abolishes the response to ACh but has no effect on either the $K_m$ or $V_{max}$ of acetylcholinesterase.

3. No correlation exists between inhibition of acetylcholinesterase by a variety of methylcarbamates and their depolarizing potencies on the electroplax. In addition, acetyl-$\beta$-methyl choline, which is specifically hydrolyzed by acetylcholinesterase, does not depolarize the electroplax.

4. Incubation of an intact skeletal muscle with pronase and other proteases abolishes the cholinesterase activity of the end plate but does not affect the response of the muscle to applied ACh. Conversely, the addition of $\alpha$-bungarotoxin to a nerve-muscle preparation will abolish a response to ACh, but acetylcholinesterase activity is unaffected.

Having disposed of the cholinesterase theory it is now incumbent upon us to state that in fact the cholinergic receptor most likely has a topography very similar to the active center of acetylcholinesterase, i.e. anionic and esteratic binding sites. This is virtually a truism, merely from a perusal of the charge distribution on the ACh molecule.

Two approaches are currently used to characterize the receptor. The first technique uses intact tissue in which a response of the tissue is measured. This approach is open to the criticism that because one is dealing with at least two events, the combination of drug and receptor and the sequential response of muscle contraction, the primary goal of studying drug-receptor interaction cannot be easily realized. Thus, not only may a problem arise of transport of an agonist or antagonist to the receptor protein but, since the coupling of an activated receptor to a tissue response is not known at a molecular level, it is conceivable that an ACh antagonist may be acting at a further point in the chain.

The second approach used to investigate the cholinergic receptor is an attempt to isolate the receptor substance. From studies on the effects of urea, heat, sulfhydryl-reacting reagents, and proteolytic enzymes, it has been adduced that receptors are proteins (but not enzymes since covalent bonds are not made or broken in the initiation of a response). Within the past two years about half a dozen laboratories have reported the isolation of the cholinergic receptor. Most of the work has been done either on *Electrophorus* or *Torpedo* electric tissue since both preparations are rich in receptor protein. The isolation procedure is usually monitored either by equilibrium dialysis to determine reversible binding of cholinergic ligands or by the irreversible binding of snake toxins, particularly $\alpha$-bungarotoxin, which has been shown to bind specifically to cholinergic receptors at neuromuscular junctions. With a variety of approaches, tissues, and techniques, there is a surprising uniformity in the characterization to date of the cholinergic receptors as isolated by different laboratories. Thus, in general, from binding experiments there appears to be about $10^4$ receptors/$\mu m^2$ of endplate which calculates out to be approximately $4 \times 10^7$ cholinergic receptors/endplate. In addition, virtually all laboratories have reported that the receptor as isolated in a solubilized form has a molecular weight of 42,000, and that a fairly good parallelism exists between binding of agonists and antagonists *in vitro* with the pharmacological activity of the agents *in vivo*. This latter observation is indeed surprising considering the fact that the receptor *in situ* is particulate and, most probably, a lipoprotein. It may turn out that this protein is only part of the receptor and that left behind in the purification process is an ionophore that functions as a channel to regulate the permeating cations that are associated with the transmitter activity of ACh.

At any rate, regardless of the procedures that are used to authenticate the isolation of the cholinergic receptor, the only really unambiguous proof will be to return the isolated receptor to an intact tissue or organ whose receptors have been inactivated and show that the application of a drug will now give the appropriate response. This may be difficult to do.

## DRUGS THAT AFFECT CENTRAL CHOLINERGIC SYSTEMS

Many of the cholinomimetics, cholinolytics, neuromuscular blocking drugs, and anticholinesterases with which the student is familiar do not affect the central nervous system because of their inability to cross the blood-brain barrier at a significant rate. However, atropine, scopolamine, and DFP (diisopropyl phosphorofluoridate) all penetrate the central nervous system, and their main effects have been studied in some detail.

The systemic injection of atropine and scopolamine leads to a decrease in the ACh content of the brain. This reduction is confined to the cerebral hemispheres. At the same time it has been shown, using the cortical cup technique, that the administration of these drugs either intravenously, intraventricularly, or via the cup resulted in the release of ACh from the exposed cortex into the collecting cup. This releasing effect of ACh by the antimuscarinic agents has also been observed in brain cortical slices. The mechanism by which these agents lower the ACh content of brain and stimulate the release is not known. What is known, however, is that the amnesic effect of atropine and scopolamine does not correlate with the lowered levels of ACh in the brain since the intraventricular injection of hemicholinum, which markedly reduces the ACh concentration in brain, has no effect on maze performance by trained rats.

The administration of oxotremorine and arecoline to rats causes a rise in the ACh content in brain which roughly coincides with the tremor period. This is presumed to be a muscarinic action of these agents since the tremor can be aborted by atropine.

A number of years ago it was observed that the long-term administration of DFP to myasthenics produced nightmares, confusion, and hallucination. Since then a number of studies using different organo-phosphorus anticholinesterases has shown behavioral effects in humans following the acute administration of these agents. Subjects have generally felt agitated, tense, and confused; on psychological tests they showed a slowing of intellectual and motor processes.

(Modified after T. Lentz, **Cell Fine Structure**, W. B. Saunders, 1971.)

There are a variety of phenylglycolate esters (e.g. *N*-ethyl-2-pyrollidylmethyl-cyclopentylphenylglycolate) which in the peripheral nervous system are classified as anticholinergic drugs. In the CNS these agents appear to be psychotomimetics; depending on the drug and the dose that is given to human subjects, effects range from apprehension to disorientation and delirium. Yohimbine and THA (1,2,3,4-tetrahydro-5-aminoacridine) were shown to antagonize the psychotomimetic effects of the glycolate esters. Interestingly enough, these two compounds are anti-cholinesterases. Physostigmine is also an antagonist but DFP and Sarin are not; these latter two compounds are hallucinatory by themselves. The conclusion to be drawn from these studies is that

FIGURE 4-2. Drugs Affecting the Neuromuscular Junction.

*Site*

| | | |
|---|---|---|
| 1. | ACh discharge promoted by | $\beta$-bungarotoxin<br>black widow spider venom<br>$La^{+++}$ |
| 2. | Release blocked by | cytochalasin B<br>botulinum toxin<br>collagenase |
| 3. | Receptor blocked by | $\alpha$-bungarotoxin<br>curare<br>decamethonium |
| 4. | Synthesis inhibited by | styryl pyridine derivatives |
| 5. | Hydrolysis inhibited by | physostygmine (eserine)<br>DFP |
| 6. | Choline uptake<br>blocked by | hemicholinium-3<br>troxypyrrolium tosylate<br>triethylcholine |

the relationship between these drugs and central cholinergic mechanisms is still mysterious.

Changes in the ACh level in brain correlated with behavioral changes in the animal first came into prominence in 1949 when it was shown that during convulsions the ACh level fell, and during sedation the ACh content of the brain rose. These observations have spawned a number of investigations in which an attempt has been made to correlate behavioral changes with the ACh content of brain. A quantity of data has been collected and many papers have been published, but this approach has yet to lead to either an elucidation of the central mechanism of action of a cholinergic drug or the delineation of a cholinergic system in the brain. Cholinergic pathways in the CNS are best identified by lesioning experiments, assays of choline acetyltransferase, and iontophoresis.

Drugs that affect the synthesis, release, and neurotransmitter activity of ACh are shown in Figure 4-2.

Hemicholinium (HC-3)

4(1-naphthylvinyl) pyridine
(NVP)

Physostigmine (Eserine)

Diisopropylphosphorofluoridate
(DFP)

Pyridine aldoxime methiodide
(2-PAM)

FIGURE 4-3. Structures of some drugs that affect the cholinergic nervous system.

SELECTED REFERENCES

Birks, R. I., and F. C. MacIntosh (1961). Acetylcholine metabolism of a sympathetic ganglion. *Can. J. Biochem. Physiol. 39*, 787.

Chan, S. L., D. Y. Shirachi, H. N. Bhargava, E. Gardner, and A. J. Trevor (1972). Purification and properties of multiple forms of brain acetylcholinesterase. *J. Neurochem. 19*, 2747.

Chao, L. P., and F. Wolfgram (1973). Purification and some properties of choline acetyltransferase (E.C. 2.3.16) from bovine brain. *J. Neurochem. 20*, 1075.

Collier, B., and H. S. Katz (1971). The synthesis, turnover and release of surplus acetylcholine in a sympathetic ganglion. *J. Physiol. 214*, 537.

Cotman, C. W., and D. A. Mathews (1971). Synaptic plasma membranes from rat brain synaptosomes. Isolation and partial characterization. *Biochem. Biophys. Acta 349*, 380.

Ehrenpreis, S., J. N. Fleisch, and T. W. Mittag (1969). Approaches to the molecular nature of pharmacological receptors. *Pharmacol. Rev. 21*, 131.

Fitzgerald, G. C., and J. R. Cooper (1971). Acetylcholine as a possible sensory mediator in rabbit corneal epithelium. *Biochem. Pharmacol. 20*, 2741.

Goldberg, A. L., and R. E. McCaman (1973). The determination of picomole amounts of acetylcholine in mammalian brain. *J. Neurochem. 20*, 1.

Hebb, C. (1972). Biosynthesis of acetylcholine in nervous tissue. *Physiol. Rev. 52*, 918.

Itokawa, Y., and J. R. Cooper (1970). Ion movements and thiamine: the release of thiamine from membrane fragments. *Biochem. Biophys. Acta 196*, 274.

Jenden, D. J. (1972). Simultaneous microestimation of choline and acetylcholine by gas chromatography/mass spectrometry/isotope dilution. *Fed. Proc. 31*, 535.

Koelle, G. B. (1961). Cytological distributions and physiological functions of cholinesterases. *Handbuch der experimentellen Pharmakologie*, XV, 268.

Leuzinger, V., M. Goldberg, and E. Carvin (1969). Molecular properties of acetylcholinesterase. *J. Mol. Biol. 40*, 217.

Nachmansohn, D. (1961). Action on axons and role of ACh in axonal conduction. *Handbuch der experimentellen Pharmakologie*, XV, 701.

O'Brien, R. D., M. E. Eldefrawi, and A. T. Eldefrawi (1972). Isolation of acetylcholine receptors. *Ann. Rev. Pharmacol. 12*, 19.

Pepeu, G. (1972). Cholinergic neurotransmission in the central nervous system. *Arch. Int. Pharm. Therap. 196*, 229.

Potter, L. T. (1970). Synthesis, storage and release of [$^{14}$C]acetylcholine in isolated rat diaphragm muscles. *J. Physiol. 206*, 145.

Whittaker, V. P., W. B. Essman, and G. H. C. Dowe (1972). The isolation of pure cholinergic synaptic vesicles from the electric organs of elasmobranch fish of the family Torpedinidae. *Biochem. J. 128*, 833.

Wilson, W. S., R. A. Schulz, and J. R. Cooper (1973). The isolation of cholinergic synaptic vesicles from bovine superior cervical ganglion and estimation of their acetylcholine content. *J. Neurochem. 20*, 659.

# 5 | Catecholamines I: General Aspects

THE TERM "catecholamine" refers, generically, to all organic compounds that contain a catechol nucleus (a benzene ring with two adjacent hydroxyl substituents) and an amine group (Fig. 5-1). In practice the term "catecholamine" usually implies dihy-

FIGURE 5-1. Catechol and catecholamine structure.

droxyphenylethylamine (dopamine, DA) and its metabolic products, norepinephrine (NE) and epinephrine (E).

The great advances in the understanding of the biochemistry, physiology, and pharmacology of norepinephrine and related compounds during the last decade have been made possible mainly through the development of new and sensitive assay techniques.

## METHODOLOGY

Bioassay procedures still remain one of the most sensitive methods for the estimation of epinephrine and norepinephrine in

TABLE 5-1. Biological Assay Preparations for Norepinephrine
and Epinephrine

| Assay Preparation | Response Measured | Sensitivity Norepineph-rine | Epineph-rine |
|---|---|---|---|
| chick rectal caecum | relaxation | 100 ng/ml | 1 ng/ml |
| blood pressure of pithed rat | increase in blood pressure | 0.1-1 ng | 5-10 ng |
| rat uterus treated with stilbestrol and contracted with carbachol | relaxation | 50 ng/ml | 0.5 ng/ml |
| perfused rabbit ear | increase in perfusion pressure | 1-5 ng | 1-5 ng |
| rat stomach strip in presence of serotonin | relaxation | 5-20 ng | 1-10 ng |

tissue extracts or biological fluids, the most notable exception being mass fragmentography, and their use is still indicated when dealing with very small amounts of these substances. Table 5-1 gives some of the various bioassay techniques employed for the catecholamines and their relative sensitivities. When the bioassay procedure is coupled with the technique of superfusion, no steps of purification and extraction are necessary and it becomes possible to measure the release and fate of vaso-active hormones directly in the circulation. However, the primary disadvantage of these assay techniques is their relative lack of specificity. The specificity of the bioassay can be increased somewhat by the use of specific antagonists and the employment of parallel assay systems in which two or more tissues with different sensitivities to the desired agent are employed. This sort of assay system has been employed very elegantly by Vane and his colleagues. Although the bioassay techniques have suitable sensitivity, they have tended to be gradually replaced by chemical methods. This is due mainly to the inherent problems of standardization and specificity.

## Fluorometric Assay

The development of sensitive fluorescent techniques for the assay of tissue catecholamines has certainly been a major factor in the rapid advancement of knowledge in this field, in part because the chemical methods do not require the skills of the rapidly vanishing "classical" pharmacologist. Furthermore, fluorescent techniques are also less time-consuming and generally less tedious than the bioassay methods. There are at present two widely used chemical procedures for the estimation of catecholamines after their conversion into fluorescent derivatives: the ethylene diamine condensation method and the trihydroxyindole method. The ethylene diamine condensation method involves the initial oxidation of catecholamines to their intermediate quinone products, which then react with ethylene diamine to form intensely fluorescent products. Since ethylene diamine will condense with many different catechol compounds to give similar fluorescent products, this method is far less specific than the trihydroxyindole reaction, and thus sometimes less useful. However, the specificity of this technique can be improved by the employment of suitable separation techniques prior to the analysis. The trihydroxyindole method which involves oxidation and cyclization is more specific and is the procedure commonly used in many laboratories for the routine assay of catecholamines. The general reaction involved in this assay procedure is illustrated in Figure 5-2. This chemical reaction appears to require the presence of a catechol nucleus, an alkyl amine substituent on the alpha carbon, and a $\beta$-hydroxyl group. Although this method is quite sensitive, the detection and estimation of very small amounts of catecholamine (i.e. plasma concentrations) are still quite difficult, due primarily to the instability of the blanks and variable quenching. Udenfriend, in his book on fluorescence assay, writes, "It is the opinion of this author that in none of the methods currently available has it been possible

Norepinephrine · 3-hydroxy 5,6 indolinedione · 3, 5, 6-trihydroxy indole

FIGURE 5-2. Trihydroxyindole reaction.

to establish the identity of apparent norepinephrine in normal plasma." However, this problem has been minimized to some extent in recent years by the employment of automated analysis techniques which have greatly improved the sample to blank ratio.

## Gas Chromatography

Gas chromatography is a notable advance in the field of analytical instrumentation, simultaneously providing a suitable means for separation, characterization, and quantitation of the complex organic mixtures encountered in tissue extracts. This technique is just beginning to be used for the identification and quantitation of catecholamines and their metabolites in biological fluids and in tissue extracts. A highly sensitive gas chromatographic technique involves the formation of halogenated catechol derivatives. These derivatives, due to their high electron affinity, make it easy to detect nanogram amounts of material by means of an electron capture detector. In most cases the trifluoroacetyl or pentafluoropropionyl derivatives have been employed because these compounds have superior chromatographic properties, are readily synthesized, and the unreacted anhydride is easily removed by volatilization. Some proven applications include the analysis of 3-methoxy-4-hydroxyphenylglycol in urine, brain and spinal fluid, analysis of 3-methoxy-4-hydroxymandelic acid in urine and the analysis of norepinephrine, normetanephrine, dopamine, and epinephrine in urine, in neuroblastoma and pheochromocytoma tissue, and most recently in brain. However, this analytical technique has not been utilized to its fullest capacity at the present time, due mainly to the inherent problems of electron capture analysis. Thus, derivative and detector instability as well as frequent contamination of these sensitive detectors presents serious obstacles which must be overcome before this technique will gain wide acceptance.

## Radioisotopic Methods

Recently some very sensitive and specific radiochemical assays have been developed for the determination of catecholamine content in biological fluid and tissue. One method is based on the conversion of norepinephrine and epinephrine to their corresponding radioactive derivatives either by incubation with S-adenosyl-L-methionine-methyl-$^{14}$C and the partially purified enzyme catechol-O-methyl transferase to form O-methyl derivatives or with phenylethanolamine-N-methyl-transferase (commercially available) to form epinephrine. A second method employs tritiated acetic anhydride to produce stable radioactive acetyl derivatives. In both of these methods addition of tracer amounts of $^3$H- or $^{14}$C-labeled catecholamines to the tissue or biological fluid prior to extraction and analysis serves to correct for any losses incurred throughout the procedure. The radioactive derivatives are then subjected to a series of rigorous purification steps prior to analysis. Determination of endogenous levels of catecholamine is then based on the $^{14}$C/$^3$H ratios of these purified derivatives. These procedures not only have greater sensitivity than the other methods described (with perhaps the exception of mass fragmentography) but in addition have the decided advantage that the calculation of the amount of amine present is based on a ratio rather than an absolute amount, with the results obtained independent of losses incurred in the purification procedures. In addition, if the radioactivity ratio remains constant through two or more chromatographic procedures, this provides intrinsic evidence of sample purity. This double isotope technique would also be adaptable to gas chromatography, where advantage of the high potential for resolution of related structural compounds can be utilized. This approach is feasible since microgram amounts of unlabeled derivatives can be added to the extracts as carrier, greatly improving the resolution and recovery aspects of this analytic technique.

## Histochemical Fluorescence Microscopy and Microspectrofluorometry

In 1955 Eränko, and also Hillarp and Hökfelt, independently observed that fluorescence microscopic examination of adrenal medullary tissue fixed in formaldehyde revealed a bright yellow fluorescence, which they attributed to catecholamines. However, attempts in sympathetically innervated tissue remained unsuccessful for a number of years, probably due to the lower amine concentrations and to the diffusion of the fluorophores into the aqueous fixative. In fact, it was not until 1961 when Falck and his coworkers described the application of freeze drying and treatment of tissue sections with dry formaldehyde vapor that a sufficiently sensitive technique became available for the purpose of demonstrating the very small amounts of catecholamines present in adrenergic nerves. Essentially, this method is based upon the conversion of various ring hydroxylated phenylethylamines, indolealkylamines, and their respective α-amino acids (even histamine)

FIGURE 5-3. Formaldehyde condensation products of biogenic monoamines. (Courtesy of L. S. Van Orden III) to highly fluorescent derivatives in the presence of relatively dry formaldehyde vapor at 60 to 80° C. This reaction appears to involve the condensation of the amino group with formaldehyde to form a new ring system. The general reactions for phenylethylamines, indolealkylamines, and histamine are illustrated in Figure 5-3. Each of these fluorescent condensation products has its own characteristic fluorescent excitation and emission maximum and therefore one can be distinguished from another spectrally.

One of the main disadvantages of this histochemical technique is that it has been virtually impossible to distinguish spectrally between the reaction products of dihydroxyphenylalanine, dopamine, norepinephrine, and epinephrine since they all form fluorophores with identical fluorescent properties. However, epinephrine and other secondary catecholamines can be distinguished from primary catecholamines because their reaction with formaldehyde requires a much longer time for completion.

Recently, Aghajanian and Roth have developed a specific pharmacological method for visualization of brain dopamine. This method is based on the observation that γ-butyrolactone produces a marked increase in brain dopamine without causing a significant increase in brain norepinephrine or serotonin and thus allows a visualization of otherwise largely undetectable fine varicose fluorescent dopamine-containing fibers. Currently, however, most investigators employ complex pharmacological methods to distinguish between norepinephrine and dopamine. Another limitation of the fluorescence method often overlooked by many investigators is that fluorescence intensity of the catecholamine fluorophores is not proportional to amine concentration over a very wide range and therefore the usefulness of this technique remains on a qualitative rather than a quantitative level. In fact, Van Orden et al. have demonstrated that the fluorescence histochemical method does not detect granular norepinephrine to the same extent as extragranular norepinephrine.

One must, however, be careful not to underestimate the significance of the contribution of fluorescence histochemistry to the study of catecholamines. The localization of catecholamines and

FIGURE 5-4. Fluorescence micrograph, of rat vas deferens. Falck-Hillarp formaldehyde vapor treatment of freeze-dried vas deferens. Magnification approximately 500 x. (Supplied through the courtesy of L. S. Van Orden, III.)

their precursors within morphologically recognizable microscopic structures has provided a great advantage to those investigators interested in studying and understanding adrenergic mechanisms (Fig. 5-4). This technique has also been employed in conjunction with electron microscopy quite successfully in the peripheral nervous system where it is possible to obtain a correlation between morphological changes (fluorescence intensity, content of granular vesicles) and monoamine content (Fig. 5-5). Obviously, the lack of such a suitable histochemical technique for the visualization of acetylcholine has proven a serious handicap for those interested in cholinergic mechanisms.

The fluorescence histochemical technique applied to the central nervous system has revealed catecholaminergic neuronal pathways and cell bodies which were previously unrecognized by the conventional methods of neuroanatomy and has made possible

FIGURE 5-5. Electron micrograph of rat vas deferens. Potassium permanganate fixation. A cross section of an adrenergic nerve terminal or "varicosity" containing many synaptic vesicles, most with electron-opaque core (i.e. granular vesicles). Magnification approximately 37,000 x. (Supplied through the courtesy of L. S. Van Orden, III.)

an extensive mapping of monoaminergic pathways in brain. (See Chapter 6.) The anterograde and retrograde changes occurring after nerve sectioning have made it possible to map the ascending and descending monoamine systems within the central nervous system. The concurrent employment of this technique with administration of new potent inhibitors of monoamine biosynthesis (see below) has made it possible to evaluate to some extent the effect of various neurotropic drugs on the activity of central monoaminergic neurons.

In the central nervous system it appears that practically the

FIGURE 5-6. Electron micrograph of normal pineal sympathetic nerve terminals exhibiting small and large granular vesicles (the latter are indicated by arrows and are approximately 1000 Å in diameter). Approximately 50 per cent of the small vesicles exhibit some degree of granularity after glutaraldehyde/osmium fixation. (Goldstein and Bloom)

entire monoamine store is contained within enlargements of the nerve terminals. These varicosities or nerve terminal regions have been estimated by fluorescence microscopy to contain very high concentrations of catecholamines, approx. 1000 to 10,000 μg/gm.

On the other hand, the monoamine cell bodies and axons have a much lower content (10-100 $\mu$g/gm). It is thought by most investigators that these varicosities, due to their relatively high amine content, are the presynaptic structures involved in transmitter storage, release, re-uptake, and synthesis.

## Electron Microscopy

In neuropharmacological research, special attention has been devoted to the problem of high resolution cytochemical methods for the identification of synaptic transmitter substances in intact

FIGURE 5-7. Low-power electron micrograph from the hypothalamus of a rat showing several axons exhibiting large granular vesicles (arrows). In the nerve terminals exhibiting large granular vesicles, smaller electron-lucent vesicles can be seen, which are of the same size as the small granular vesicles seen in the pineal nerve ending of Fig. 5-9. The nucleus of an ependymal cell can be seen at lower right.

FIGURE 5-8. High-power view of nerve terminal from the cerebellar cortex exhibiting both small electron-lucent synaptic vesicles and large granular vesicles of varying internal electron opacity (arrows). Mitochondria (M) and numerous small electron-lucent synaptic vesicles can also be seen within this nerve terminal.

nervous tissue, since this essential criterion must be satisfied in order to identify a substance as the likely transmitter for a particular defined synaptic complex. Thus electron microscopy coupled with the proper cytochemical techniques has provided the investigator in the catecholamine field with a technique for visualization of granular vesicles within the neuron suspected but not proven to contain catecholamines. Figures 5-5 to 5-8, electron micrographs of rat vas deferens, pineal gland, hypothalamus, and cerebellar cortex, illustrate the various types of vesicular structures found in these tissues. In peripheral noradrenergic neurons there is a good correlation between norepinephrine depletion and the disappearance of the dense core from vesicles.

A new and rather unusual pharmacological agent has been discovered which should be helpful in the study of adrenergic mechanisms. This compound is 6-hydroxydopamine (3, 4, 6-tri-hydroxyphenylethylamine). When administered intravenously or intraventricularly this compound is rapidly and efficiently taken up into the sympathetic nerve endings. Perhaps because of its selective distribution and concentration as well as its extreme susceptibility to oxidation, this agent appears selectively to destroy sympathetic neurons by causing acute degeneration of adrenergic terminals. In effect this compound produces a "chemical sympathectomy." Thus, when the compound is given intravenously to animals it causes almost total depletion of norepinephrine in sympathetically innervated tissues and also greatly reduces tyrosine hydroxylase activity. The only exception appears to be the adrenal medulla where 6-hydroxydopamine is not effectively taken up and the resultant demands placed on this organ to maintain homeostasis leads to a significant increase in tyrosine hydroxylase activity in this organ. In most aspects, "chemical sympathectomy" produces effects comparable to those produced by surgical denervation or immunosympathectomy produced by the administration of anti-sera to Nerve Growth Factor. However, this technique has the additional advantage that it may be applied to the central nervous system. Thus, when this agent is given intraventricularly or intracerebrally, it produces an extensive and lasting depletion of brain norepinephrine and dopamine and a degeneration of central dopamine- and norepinephrine-containing neurons. The depletion and degeneration are the result of what appears to be quite selective destruction of catecholamine-containing neurons by 6-hydroxydopamine. Since it has been shown that this agent acts specifically only to destroy catecholaminergic neurons, it might well serve as a tool for the evaluation of some of the functional roles ascribed to catecholamines in the central nervous system.

## DISTRIBUTION

No matter what our particular specialty in neuropharmacology, we are all ultimately interested in how the agent or agents we wish to study are distributed in the nervous system.

In 1946 von Euler in Sweden and shortly later Holtz in Germany independently identified the presence of norepinephrine in adrenergic nerves. These findings laid the foundation for a new era of research in the field of catecholamines. At that time it was not technically possible to study the content of transmitter in the terminal parts of the adrenergic fiber. Despite this, Euler predicted that norepinephrine was, in fact, highly concentrated in the nerve terminal region from which it was released to act as a neurotransmitter. This prediction was conclusively documented some ten years later with the development of the fluorescence histochemical technique.

A systematic study of extracts of various mammalian nerves by Euler and his colleagues demonstrated that there was a very close correlation between the content of norepinephrine present and the proportion of nonmyelinated to myelinated nerve fibers. Sympathetic ganglia were also found to contain norepinephrine in a concentration similar to that found in the postganglionic fibers. Of all the nerves studied, splenic nerve was found to have the highest content of norepinephrine. This finding is in agreement with histochemical and physiological evidence which indicates that this nerve is made up almost exclusively of small nonmyelinated adrenergic fibers. This tissue serves therefore as an excellent model system to study synthesis and storage of the sympathetic neurotransmitter. The correlation between the norepinephrine content of a nerve or an organ and its content of adrenergic fibers is now so well established that the occurrence of norepinephrine in a given organ or nerve can, in general, be

TABLE 5.2. Tissue Distribution of Norepinephrine
($\mu$g/gm)

| Organ | Species | | | |
|---|---|---|---|---|
| | Bovine | Cat | Rabbit | Rat |
| artery | 0.2-1.0 | | | |
| heart | 0.48 | 0.5-1.0 | 1.4[b] | 0.65 |
| liver | 0.25 | 0.005-0.20 | | 0.06 |
| lung | 0.05 | | 0.05-0.07[b] | |
| skeletal muscle | 0.04 | 0.03 | | |
| spleen | 1.5-3.5 | 0.8-1.4 | 0.3-0.5 | 0.40 |
| splenic nerve | 8.5-18.5 | | | |
| vas deferens | 9.3[a] | 4.4[a] | 6.7[a] | 7.9[a] |
| vein | 0.1-0.5 | | 1.0-2.5[b] | |

Unless indicated otherwise data taken from table 18—U.S. von Euler, Noradrenaline

[a] W. O. Sjostrand, Acta Physiol. Scand. 65, Suppl. 257, 1965.
[b] R. H. Roth and J. Hughes, unpublished data.

taken as evidence for the presence of adrenergic fibers provided the presence of chromaffin tissue can be excluded. Table 5-2 illustrates the distribution of norepinephrine in various organs and tissues. Thus, tissues with a high density of sympathetic innervation have a relatively high concentration of sympathetic transmitter, norepinephrine, and vice versa. The ubiquitous distribution of norepinephrine in tissue is consistent with the presence of adrenergic vasomotor fibers in almost all peripheral tissue. The absence of norepinephrine in placenta or bone marrow is in agreement with histochemical and physiological evidence, which suggests that these tissues also lack any adrenergic vasomotor innervation.

Shortly after it was established that norepinephrine was the neurotransmitter substance of adrenergic nerves in the peripheral nervous system, norepinephrine was identified by Holtz as a normal constituent of mammalian brain. However, for some years it was believed that the presence of norepinephrine in mammalian brain only reflected vasomotor innervation to the cerebral blood vessels. It was not until 1954 that Vogt demonstrated that norepinephrine was not uniformly distributed in the central nervous system and that this nonuniform distribution did not in any way coincide with the density of blood vessels found in a given brain area. This characteristic regional localization of norepinephrine within mammalian brain suggested that norepinephrine might subserve some specialized function perhaps as a central neurotransmitter. In fact, this observation undoubtedly supplied the impetus for many investigators to pursue actively the functional reasons for the nonuniform presence of this active substance in the central nervous system. The relative distribution of norepinephrine is quite similar in most mammalian species. The highest concentration is usually found in the hypothalamus and other areas of central sympathetic representation. More norepinephrine is generally found in gray matter than in white matter.

Dopamine is also found in the mammalian central nervous system and its distribution differs markedly from that of norepinephrine, suggesting that dopamine is present not only as a precursor of norepinephrine. In fact, it represents more than 50 per cent of the total catecholamine content of the central nervous system of most mammals. The highest levels of dopamine are found in the neostriatum, nucleus accumbens, and tuberculum olfactorium. The presence of abundant dopamine in the basal ganglia has stimulated intensive research on the functional aspects of this compound. There is a growing wealth of evidence which suggests that this agent may have an important role in extrapyramidal function. (See Chapter 6.) Dopamine is also present in the superior cervical ganglion, where it may play a role other than as a precursor of norepinephrine. The superior cervical ganglion appears to have at least three distinct populations of neurons: cholinergic neurons, noradrenergic neurons, and small intensely fluorescent (SIF) cells. The SIF cells are believed to be the small interneurons which contain dopamine. The actual functional significance of these SIF cells is at the present time unknown although it has been

TABLE 5-3. Catecholamine Distribution in the Central Nervous System

| Brain Region | Species | Dopamine μg/gm | Norepinephrine μg/gm |
|---|---|---|---|
| whole brain | dog | 0.19 | 0.16 |
| whole brain | rabbit | 0.32 | 0.29 |
| whole brain | rat | 0.60 | 0.49 |
| whole brain | cat | 0.28 | 0.22 |
| medulla oblongata | dog | 0.13 | 0.37 |
| medulla oblongata | rat | — | 0.72 |
| mesencephalon | dog | 0.10 | 0.41 |
| cerebellum | rat | — | 0.17 |
| cerebellar cortex | dog | 0.03 | 0.06 |
| hypothalamus | rat | 0.14 | 1.29 |
| hypothalamus | dog | — | 1.00 |
| hypothalamus | cat | — | 1.40 |
| striatum | rat | 7.50 | 0.25 |
| caudate nucleus | rat | 6.39 | 0.27 |
| caudate nucleus | cat | 9.90 | 0.10 |
| caudate nucleus | dog | 5.90 | 0.10 |
| lentiform nucleus | dog | 1.63 | 0.08 |
| cerebral cortex | dog | — | 0.05 |
| cerebral cortex | rat | 0.01 | 0.18 |

Data taken from: L. L. Iversen, *The Uptake and Storage of Noradrenaline in Sympathetic Nerves*, Cambridge Univ. Press. 1967, p. 34.

suggested that dopamine released from these interneurons is responsible for hyperpolarization of the ganglion. (See cyclic AMP section, Chapter 9.) Table 5-3 summarizes the regional brain distribution of norepinephrine and dopamine in various mammalian species.

Epinephrine concentration in the mammalian central nervous system is relatively low, approximately 5 to 17 per cent (by bioassay) of the norepinephrine content. Many investigators have suggested that these estimates are subject to error and have therefore discounted the importance of the occurrence of epinephrine in mammalian brain. However, recently it has been demonstrated that certain brain areas such as the olfactory bulb and olfactory tubercle contain substantial amounts of the enzyme phenyletha-nolamine-N-methyl transferase and therefore are capable of forming epinephrine *in vivo*. At present, the significance of the presence or synthetic capacity for epinephrine in certain brain areas is unknown, but it is conceivable that epinephrine might play some role as a neurohumoral agent in mammalian olfactory structures.

A detailed topographical survey of brain catecholamines at different levels of organization within the central nervous system has helped to give us some sort of basic framework from which to organize and conduct logical experiments concerning the possible function of these amines.

## *Intraneuronal Localization*

With the refinement of physical and chemical techniques it became possible to further localize monoamines both in isolated subcellular particles obtained by differential and density gradient centrifugation and by fluorescence histochemistry and electron microscopy in axonal varicosities. These powerful techniques have provided us with our current concepts concerning the location of amines within the neuron in a structure referred to as synaptic vesicles. The concept of storage of monoamines, however, will be covered in more detail when we consider the life cycle of the catecholamines.

## LIFE CYCLE OF THE CATECHOLAMINES

## *Biosynthesis*

Catecholamines are formed in brain, chromaffin cells, sympathetic nerves, and sympathetic ganglia from their amino acid precursor tyrosine by a sequence of enzymatic steps first postulated by Blaschko in 1939 and finally confirmed by Nagatsu and

FIGURE 5-9. Primary and alternative pathways in the formation of catecholamines:

1. Tyrosine hydroxylase  2. Aromatic amino acid decarboxylase
3. Dopamine-β-oxidase  4. Phenylethanolamine-N-methyl transferase  5. Non-specific N-methyl transferase in lung; folate-dependent N-methyl transferase in brain.  6. Catechol-forming enzyme.

coworkers in 1964 with the demonstration that an enzyme (tyrosine hydroxylase) was involved in the conversion of L-tyrosine to DOPA. This amino acid precursor, tyrosine, is normally present in the circulation in a concentration of about 5 to 8 $\times$ 10$^{-5}$M. It is taken up from the bloodstream and concentrated within the brain and presumably also in other sympathetically innervated tissue by an active transport mechanism. Once inside the peripheral neuron tyrosine undergoes a series of chemical transformations resulting in the ultimate formation of norepinephrine or in brain, norepinephrine, dopamine, or epinephrine, depending upon the availability of phenylethanolamine-N-methyl transferase or dopa-

Octopamine → Synephrine

Norepinephrine → Epinephrine

Epinine

N-Methyl epinephrine

mine $\beta$-hydroxylase. This biosynthetic pathway for the formation of catecholamines is illustrated in Figure 5-9. The conversion of tyrosine to norepinephrine and epinephrine was first demonstrated in the adrenal medulla. More recently, the availability of radio-active precursors of high specific activity and chromatographic separation techniques has allowed the confirmation of the above-mentioned pathway to norepinephrine in sympathetic nerves, ganglia, heart, arterial and venous tissue, and brain. In mammals, tyrosine can be derived from dietary phenylalanine by a hydroxylase (phenylalanine hydroxylase) found primarily in liver. Both phenylalanine and tyrosine are normal constituents of mammalian

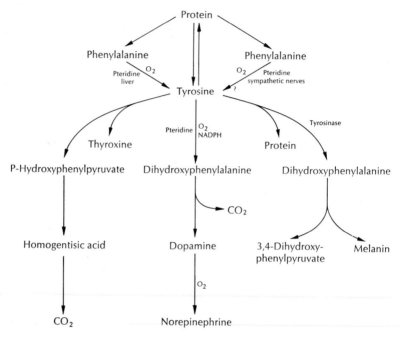

FIGURE 5-10. Metabolism of tyrosine.

brain, present in a free form in a concentration of about $5 \times 10^{-5}M$. However, norepinephrine biosynthesis is usually considered to begin with tyrosine which represents a branch point for many important biosynthetic processes in animal tissues (Fig. 5-10). It should be emphasized that the percentage of tyrosine utilized for catecholamine biosynthesis as opposed to other biochemical pathways is very minimal.

1. *Tyrosine hydroxylase.* The first enzyme in the biosynthetic pathway, tyrosine hydroxylase, was the last enzyme in this series of reactions to be identified. It was demonstrated by Udenfriend and his colleagues in 1964 and its properties have recently been reviewed. It is present in the adrenal medulla, brain, and in all sympathetically innervated tissue studied to date. This enzyme appears to be a unique constituent of catecholamine-containing neurons and chromaffin cells; it completely disappears from

renal, salivary gland, vas deferens, and cardiac tissue upon chronic sympathetic denervation. The enzyme is stereospecific, requires molecular $O_2$, $Fe^{++}$, and a tetrahydropteridine cofactor, and shows a fairly high degree of substrate specificity. Thus, this enzyme, in contrast to tyrosinase, oxidizes only the naturally occurring amino acid, L-tyrosine, and to a smaller extent L-phenylalanine. D-Tyrosine, tyramine, or L-tryptophan will not serve as substrates for the enzyme. However, phenylalanine hydroxylase and tyrosine hydroxylase appear to be distinct enzymes since phenylalanine hydroxylase does not hydroxylate tyrosine and is not inhibited by some potent tyrosine hydroxylase inhibitors. It has been suggested, but not proven, that the cofactor for tyrosine hydroxylase may be dihydrobiopterin, the compound demonstrated to be a naturally occurring cofactor for phenylalanine hydroxylase. The majority of experiments suggests that the enzyme is present in the particulate-free fraction of nerve or adrenal medullary homogenate, although some evidence exists to the contrary. In brain the enzyme is associated with the synaptosome fraction.

The $K_m$ for the enzymatic conversion of tyrosine to DOPA by purified adrenal tyrosine hydroxylase is about $2 \times 10^{-5}M$, and in a preparation of brain synaptosomes about $0.4 \times 10^{-5}M$. Tyrosine hydroxylation appears to be the rate limiting step in the biosynthesis of norepinephrine in the peripheral nervous system and is likely to be the rate limiting step in the formation of norepinephrine and dopamine in the brain as well. In most sympathetically innervated tissues including the brain, the activity of DOPA decarboxylase and that of dopamine-$\beta$-oxidase have a magnitude 100 to 1000 times that of tyrosine hydroxylase. This lower activity of tyrosine hydroxylase may be due either to the presence of less enzyme or to a lower turnover number of the enzyme. Since this enzyme has been demonstrated to be the rate limiting step in catecholamine biosynthesis it is logical that pharmacological intervention at this step would cause a reduction of norepinephrine biosynthesis. Many earlier attempts to produce chemical sympathectomy by blockade of the last two steps in the synthesis of norepinephrine have proved largely unsuccessful.

On the other hand, studies with inhibitors of tyrosine hydroxylase have proved to be much more successful, producing a marked reduction in endogenous norepinephrine and dopamine in brain and norepinephrine in heart, spleen, and other sympathetically innervated tissues. Effective inhibitors of this enzymatic step can be categorized by four main groups: (1) amino acid analogues; (2) catechol derivatives; (3) tropolones and (4) selective iron chelators. Some effective amino acid analogues include α-methyl-$p$-tyrosine and its ester, α-methyl-3-iodotyrosine, 3-iodotyrosine and α-methyl-5-hydroxytryptophan. In general, α-methyl-amino acids are more potent than the unmethylated analogues, and a marked increase in activity in the case of the tyrosine analogues can also be produced by substituting a halogen at the 3 position of the benzene ring. Most of the agents in this category act as competitive inhibitors of the substrate tyrosine. In this respect α-methyl-5-hydroxytryptophan appears to be unique, since it does not appear to compete with substrate or pteridine cofactor. Its actual mechanism at the present time remains unknown. The potent halogenated tyrosine analogues such as 3-iodotyrosine are about 100 times as active as α-methyl-$p$-tyrosine *in vitro*, but they are substantially less active *in vivo*. This is probably due to the very rapid deiodination of these compounds to tyrosine or tyrosine analogues which occurs *in vivo*. α-Methyl-$p$-tyrosine and its methyl ester have been the inhibitors most widely used to demonstrate the effects of exercise, stress, and various drugs on the turnover of catecholamines and also to lower norepinephrine formation in patients with pheochromocytoma and malignant hypertension.

*Dihydroxyphenylalanine Decarboxylase*

The second enzyme involved in catecholamine biosynthesis is DOPA decarboxylase, which was actually the first catecholamine synthetic enzyme to be discovered. Although originally believed to remove carboxyl groups only from L-DOPA, a study of purified enzyme preparations and specific inhibitors has subsequently demonstrated that this DOPA decarboxylase acts on all naturally occurring aromatic L-amino acids, including histidine, tyrosine, tryptophan, and phenylalanine as well as both DOPA and 5-hydroxytryptophan. Therefore, this enzyme is more appropriately referred to as "L-aromatic amino acid decarboxylase." There is no appreciable binding of this enzyme to particles within the cell, since when tissues are disrupted and the resultant homogenates centrifuged at high speeds, the decarboxylase activity remains associated largely with the supernatant fraction. The exception to this is in brain where some of the decarboxylase activity is associated with synaptosomes. However, since synaptosomes are in essence pinched-off nerve endings they would be expected to retain entrapped cytoplasm as well as other intracellular organelles. DOPA-decarboxylase is, relative to other enzymes in the biosynthetic pathway for norepinephrine formation, very active and requires pyridoxal phosphate (vitamin $B_6$) as a cofactor. The apparant $K_m$ value for this enzyme is $4 \times 10^{-4}M$. The high activity of this enzyme may explain why it has been difficult to detect endogenous DOPA in sympathetically innervated tissue and brain. It is rather ubiquitous in nature, occurring in the cytoplasm of most tissue including the liver, stomach, brain, and kidney in high levels, suggesting that its function in metabolism is not limited solely to catecholamine biosynthesis. Although decarboxylase activity can be reduced by production of vitamin $B_6$ deficiency in animals, this does not usually result in a reduction of tissue catecholamines although it appears to interfere with the rate of repletion of adrenal catecholamines after insulin depletion. In addition, potent decarboxylase inhibitors also have very little effect on endogenous levels of norepinephrine in tissue.

*Dopamine-β-oxidase*

Although it has been known for many years that brain, sympathetically innervated tissue, sympathetic ganglia, and adrenal medulla could transform dopamine into norepinephrine, it was not until 1960 that the enzyme responsible for this conversion was isolated from the adrenal medulla. This enzyme requires molecular oxygen and ascorbate and has a $K_m$ of about $5 \times 10^{-3}M$. Dicarboxylic acids such as fumaric acid are not absolute requirement, but they stimulate the reaction. Dopamine-$\beta$-hydroxylase is a $Cu^{++}$-containing protein, with about two moles of cupric ion/mole of enzyme. It appears to be associated with the particulate fraction from heart, brain, sympathetic nerve, and adrenal medulla, and it is currently believed that this enzyme is localized primarily in the membrane of the amine storage granules. This enzyme usually disappears after chronic sympathetic denervation and therefore is believed present largely only in adrenergic neurons or adrenal chromaffin tissue. Dopamine $\beta$-hydroxylase does not show a high degree of substrate specificity and acts *in vitro* on a variety of substrates besides dopamine, oxidizing almost any phenylethylamine to its corresponding phenylethanolamine (i.e. tyramine $\longrightarrow$ octopamine, $\alpha$-methyldopamine $\longrightarrow$ $\alpha$-methylnorepinephrine). A number of the resultant, structurally analogous metabolites can replace norepinephrine at the noradrenergic nerve endings and function as "false neurotransmitters."

Dopamine-$\beta$-oxidase can be inhibited by a wide variety of compounds. The most effective are compounds which chelate copper: D-cysteine and L-cysteine, glutathione, mercaptoethanol, and coenzyme A. The inhibition can be reversed by addition of N-ethylmaleimide, which reacts with the sulfhydryl groups and interferes with the chelating properties of these substances. Copper chelating agents such as diethyldithiocarbamate and FLA-63 [bis-(1-methyl-4-homopiperazinyl-thiocarbonyl)-disulfide] have proved to be effective inhibitors both *in vivo* and *in vitro*. Thus it has been possible to treat animals with disulfuram and produce a reduction in brain norepinephrine and an elevation of brain dopamine. This manipulation might serve as a useful tool in the assessment of the relative roles of norepinephrine and dopamine in the central nervous system. However, in most cases, especially in the periphery, the dopamine which is not $\beta$-hydroxylated to norepinephrine does not accumulate to any great extent since it appears to be very rapidly deaminated by monoamine oxidase (MAO).

The major increase, corresponding to the missing norepinephrine, is usually found in dopamine metabolites. Some recent work has indicated that endogenous inhibitors are found in tissue homogenates which when removed lead to a significant enhancement of dopamine-$\beta$-hydroxylase activity. It has been suggested that these inhibitors may have a role in the regulation of norepinephrine biosynthesis *in vivo* but it is also possible that they are artifacts of homogenization.

Since dopamine-$\beta$-oxidase obtained from the bovine adrenal medulla can be prepared in a relatively pure form, it has been possible to produce a specific antibody to the enzyme. This antibody inactivates bovine dopamine-$\beta$-hydroxylase but does not appear to cross react with either DOPA decarboxylase or tyrosine hydroxylase. However, cross reactivity between dopamine-$\beta$-hydroxylase from human, guinea pig, and dog with the antibody against the bovine enzyme was observed and indicates that the enzymes from these various sources are probably structurally related. By coupling immunochemical techniques with fluorescence and electron microscopy, this antibody has already proved useful in localization of this enzyme in intact tissue.

*Phenylethanolamine-N-methyl Transferase*

In the adrenal medulla norepinephrine is $N$-methylated by the enzyme phenylethanolamine-$N$-methyltransferase to form epinephrine. This enzyme is largely restricted to the adrenal medulla although low levels of activity have been reported in heart and mammalian brain, especially in areas involved with olfaction. Like the decarboxylase, this enzyme also appears in the supernatant of homogenates. Demonstration of activity requires the presence of the methyl donor $S$-adenosyl methionine. The adrenal medullary enzyme shows poor substrate specificity and will transfer methyl groups to the nitrogen atom on a variety of $\beta$-hydroxylated amines. However, this adrenal enzyme is distinct from the nonspecific $N$-methyltransferase of rabbit lung, which in addition to $N$-methylating phenylethanolamine derivatives will also react with many normally occurring indoleamines and such diverse structures as phenylisopropylamine, aromatic amines, and phenanthrenes. Recently an *N*-methyl transferase has been found in brain which uses 5-methyl-tetrahydrofolate as the methyl donor and dopamine as a substrate. This provides an alternate pathway for epinephrine formation as well as a pathway for epinine formation in brain.

*Synthesis Regulation*

Knowledge concerning the various enzymes involved in the synthesis of dopamine, norepinephrine, and epinephrine have provided an excellent example of how extensive information of the individual components of a given biological system can contribute to a better understanding of its over-all function. Thus, once it was established that tyrosine hydroxylase was the rate-limiting step in the conversion of tyrosine to norepinephrine it did not take long to realize and to demonstrate experimentally that potent inhibitors of this initial step would effectively reduce tissue levels of norepinephrine. However, even as it becomes possible to understand more fully the chemistry and functional aspects of these enzymes under isolated conditions, this information still proves to be inadequate for a complete understanding of how, in fact, these enzymes function *in vivo*. It is necessary to have an appreciation of the cytological arrangement of the enzymes and cofactors within the neuron as well as some insight as to the external factors which may influence the activity of the neuron. Therefore it is becoming more and more important for neuropharmacologists to have a broad basic training and to take the time to try to interrelate the *in vivo* and *in vitro* data obtained experimentally to see if they can be correlated to provide a better understanding of the physiological control mechanisms involved.

It has been known for a long time that the degree of sympathetic activity does not influence the endogenous levels of norepinephrine; and it has been speculated that there must be some homeostatic mechanism whereby the level of transmitter is maintained at a relatively constant level in the sympathetic nerve endings despite the additional losses assumed to occur during enhanced sympathetic activity.

Recent experimental evidence now suggests that the ring hydroxylation of tyrosine to DOPA is regulated both *in vivo* and *in vitro* by sympathetic nerve activity: (1) Decentralization results in decreased conversion of tyrosine to catecholamines while the conversion of DOPA and dopamine to norepinephrine remains unaffected. (2) Increased sympathetic activity either *in vivo* or *in vitro* accelerates the formation of catecholamines from tyrosine but not from labeled DOPA. (3) Hypotensive drugs such as $\alpha$-adrenergic blocking agents markedly increase the formation of norepinephrine from $^{14}$C-tyrosine, an effect which can be blocked by ganglionic blocking agents. (4) Various phenothiazines, notably chlorpromazine, accelerate dopamine biosynthesis in the central nervous system presumably by causing a compensatory activation of dopaminergic neurons. In each of these cases the enzymatic biosynthetic step which is accelerated appears to be the rate-limiting hydroxylation of tyrosine. At least in the peripheral nervous system, this effect appears to be localized at the nerve terminals since stimulation of isolated sympathetic axons does not result in an acceleration of norepinephrine biosynthesis.

The actual mechanism(s) by which increased neuronal activity accelerates synthesis remains obscure. A number of interesting possibilities present themselves: (1) Since norepinephrine and dopamine can inhibit tyrosine hydroxylase *in vitro*, it has been suggested that depletion of a small interneuronal pool of norepinephrine strategically associated with the enzyme may stimulate tyrosine hydroxylase activity. Thus, the end product, norepinephrine or dopamine, could act as feedback inhibitors of the rate-limiting enzyme. (2) Increased nervous activity could directly increase the amount of enzyme (tyrosine hydroxylase) protein either by causing an increase in the synthesis of tyrosine hydroxylase or by inhibiting the normal turnover or destruction of the enzyme protein. (3) Neuronal activity could result in a release of a "local hormone" that influences enzymatic activity. (4) The ion fluxes occurring during nerve stimulation could increase enzymatic activity possibly by an allosteric effect, resulting in a conformational change in the enzyme protein. (5) Nerve activation could alter the uptake of tyrosine into a specific site where it is selectively converted to DOPA.

Since short-term increases in neuronal activity, either *in vitro* or *in vivo*, do not increase the actual amount of tyrosine hydroxylase, enzyme induction is unlikely to be responsible for the apparent increase in its activity. Although, after massive nerve stimulation of the vas deferens the post-stimulation increase in tyrosine to norepinephrine conversion can be antagonized by puromycin, this observation does not necessarily imply an increase in the synthesis of tyrosine hydroxylase. In fact, recent studies indicate that electrical stimulation for time intervals up to 4 hours produces no increase in the amount of tyrosine hydroxylase found in the tissue. Also, prolonged depolarization of this tissue with $K^+$ which results in more than a 100 per cent increase in norepinephrine biosynthesis *does not* result in an increase in tyrosine hydroxylase.

Allosteric activators of tyrosine hydroxylase have been considered, but experiments on partially purified adrenal medullary tyrosine hydroxylase showed no activation with various endogenous substances which might be expected to be released on nerve stimulation (that is, $Na^+$, $K^+$, $Ca^{++}$, acetylcholine, ATP, AMP, $NAD^+$, etc.). Furthermore, there is no evidence that the protein is, in fact, allosteric in nature. However, experiments conducted on an adrenal medullary enzyme may not apply to tyrosine hydroxylase isolated from sympathetic neurons. It is quite conceivable that tyrosine hydroxylase isolated from different sources could have substantially different properties. Recent experiments demonstrating that mucopolysaccharides can activate brain tyrosine hydroxylase may prove to be important.

Many experiments indirectly support the first possibility, that regulation occurs at the tyrosine hydroxylase step through a mechanism involving end product inhibition. Tyrosine hydroxylase from sympathetic nerves or adrenal medulla is inhibited *in vitro* by various catecholamines, apparently by competition with pteridine cofactor. *In vitro* addition of norepinephrine to the incubation media ($10^{-6}$M) blocks the nerve-stimulation-induced acceleration of norepinephrine biosynthesis in the vas deferens. Also, addition of norepinephrine to normal, nonstimulated vasa deferentia, brain slices, or heart slices results in a marked inhibition of norepinephrine biosynthesis. Additional studies have demonstrated that elevation of brain or heart catecholamine levels pharmacologically, by inhibition of monoamine oxidase, results in a substantial reduction of catecholamine biosynthesis in these tissues.

Recently, conditions other than direct nerve stimulation have been demonstrated to accelerate norepinephrine biosynthesis. Thus, the naturally occurring polypeptide angiotensin II, in amounts as low as $10^{-9}$M, significantly increases norepinephrine formation. Also incubation of sympathetically innervated tissue in a high potassium medium results in a marked increase in catecholamine biosynthesis. This latter effect is apparent in tissue of both central and peripheral origin. Although the exact molecular mechanism in accelerating norepinephrine biosynthesis is still unknown at the present time, these agents may serve as effective tools for dissection of the molecular events involved in the regulation of norepinephrine biosynthesis.

It would be naïve to believe that catecholamine biosynthesis would not also be influenced by circulating hormones. In fact, steroid hormones will increase phenylethanolamine-*N*-methyltransferase activity both in the adrenal gland and in the central nervous system. Furthermore, thyroidectomy increases the conversion of $^{14}$C-tyrosine to $^{14}$C-norepinephrine. This finding suggests that normal degradation products of thyroid hormone (i.e. iodinated tyrosines) may be circulating in the bloodstream and acting as endogenous inhibitors of catecholamine biosynthesis. This, however, seems unlikely in normal individuals due to the presence of very active tissue dehalogenases. In certain patients with a defect in tissue dehalogenase this could become a reality, since it is known that in this instance iodotyrosines accumulate in the body and may reach levels expected to significantly inhibit tyrosine hydroxylase.

Even though tyrosine hydroxylase has been demonstrated to be rate limiting under most circumstances, this reaction may not remain rate limiting under all physiological conditions. Since there is a sequence of reactions, any one of these steps could assume a rate-limiting role depending upon the given pathological or pharmacologically induced situations. Thus, reserpine can transform the dopamine-$\beta$-hydroxylase step into the rate-limiting step presumably by blocking access of the substrate dopamine to the site of its conversion to norepinephrine. In fact, experiments utilizing the bovine splenic nerve granule as a model system have indicated that extragranular norepinephrine can effectively inhibit the uptake of dopamine into the granules and thus also inhibit the conversion of dopamine to norepinephrine. However, whether or not this sort of mechanism is functional *in vivo* (i.e. if high concentrations of cytoplasmic norepinephrine can inhibit the conversion of dopamine to norepinephrine) remains to be demonstrated.

*Alternative Biosynthetic Pathways*

The question has often been raised as to whether the sequence of enzymatic reactions described in detail above is in fact obligatory. Many attempts have been made to find alternative pathways *in vivo*, and to determine whether they are functionally important. Thus if labeled tyramine is administered to animals, both labeled norepinephrine and normetanephrine can be isolated in the urine. It has been very difficult to detect the conversion of tyramine to norepinephrine in sympathetically innervated tissue. However, the conversion of tyramine to dopamine has been demonstrated in liver microsomes. Therefore, it is possible that this conversion of tyramine to norepinephrine observed *in vivo* is a reflection of a metabolic reaction taking place in the liver rather than in the sympathetic neuron.

*Turnover*

The term "turnover" connotes the over-all rate at which the whole amine store within a given tissue is replaced. Thus, turnover rates are not necessarily identical with rates of biosynthesis. However, estimation of turnover rate can be used as an index to the functional state of various populations of sympathetic neurons, although not as an index of the synthetic capacity of the neurons.

Currently, many techniques are being utilized for the assessment of catecholamine turnover in both peripheral and central sympathetic neurons.

1. Turnover of norepinephrine has been estimated by measurement of the rate of decline of the specific activity of norepinephrine after a tracer dose of labeled amine is introduced into the endogenous pool. This technique has been applied both to peripheral and central neurons. In the case of the central nervous system the problem of penetration of the blood-brain barrier has been circumvented by administration of the labeled amine by intracisternal or intraventricular injections. This method for measurement of turnover, as one might expect, has a number of limitations. This method assumes that all the labeled norepinephrine found in the brain and in peripheral sympathetically innervated tissue is specifically retained by only the norepinephrine-containing neurons. This is not the case, since in addition to its retention in norepinephrine-containing neurons, labeled norepinephrine is also taken up and retained by a central network of dopamine-containing neurons in the central nervous system. In most cases this is not a serious limitation in the central nervous system since, except for the dopamine terminals in the striatum, olfactory tubercle, nucleus accumbens and the median eminence, the remainder of the brain contains only a relatively small number of dopamine-containing terminals.

The isotope method assumes that only tracer amounts of labeled norepinephrine are introduced into the endogenous pool so that the size of the endogenous pool remains unaltered. This limitation has been largely overcome with the availability of norepinephrine of high specific activity and it is now possible to administer amounts of labeled norepinephrine which alter endogenous levels of amines by less than 5 per cent. Perhaps the greatest disadvantage of this method, which also applies to many other methods used to measure turnover, is the assumption that norepinephrine is stored in a single homogeneous pool with which the labeled norepinephrine mixes completely. In view of much biochemical, histochemical, and pharmacological evidence indicating more than one "pool" of catecholamines in sympathetic neurons, this assumption appears somewhat unlikely.

2. Another technique for measuring norepinephrine turnover involves following the disappearance rate of endogenous norepinephrine after inhibition of catecholamine biosynthesis by $\alpha$-methyl-$p$-tyrosine or another potent inhibitor of tyrosine hydroxylase. This technique also suffers from several disadvantages. First, it involves measurement of an exponentially decreasing level of norepinephrine which is difficult to measure accurately in small tissue samples. Second, the required administration of large amounts of drugs (synthesis inhibitors) are almost certain to induce pharmacological actions aside from their "specific" action on tyrosine hydroxylase. Third, since turnover is being measured while endogenous levels of norepinephrine are being markedly depleted, this extensive depletion may in itself influence the normal control processes existing in the neuron.

3. An alternative isotopic method is to administer catecholamine precursors such as tyrosine or DOPA which are ultimately converted to labeled dopamine and norepinephrine. Catecholamine turnover is then determined by applying principles of steady state kinetics to the decline of norepinephrine and/or dopamine specific activities. The disadvantage of this method is that the results are complicated by the persistence of labeled catecholamine precursors in the circulation and tissues for considerable lengths of time after administration. This complication can be minimized to some extent by "chasing" the label with unlabeled precursor in order effectively to dilute the specific activity of the original agent.

4. Another isotope method involves the administration of labeled tyrosine and calculation of the rate of catecholamine synthesis from the rate of conversion of labeled tyrosine to labeled catecholamine. Provided that (a) endogenous catecholamine tissue levels remain unchanged, (b) that total tissue norepinephrine is derived from synthesis, and (c) that newly synthesized norepinephrine is not utilized (released or metabolized) preferentially, this technique provides a useful estimate of turnover.

5. More indirect methods for estimation of amine turnover in the central nervous system involve the measurement of amine metabolites released into ventricular perfusion fluids or their concentration changes in the cerebrospinal fluid (CSF) or in brain tissue. An advantage of the CSF metabolite approach is its possible clinical application. It should be immediately pointed out that the degree of accumulation of a given metabolite in the central nervous system or cerebrospinal fluid is not necessarily an index of the quantity of metabolite formed, since most primary catecholamine metabolites can undergo further metabolism and be removed from the central nervous system or cerebrospinal fluid at different rates. Also drugs or various physiological conditions can alter routes of metabolism as well as rates of removal from the brain or cerebrospinal fluid independent of their effects on amine turnover. When estimation of metabolic end products of cerebral amine metabolism are used as indices to turnover, the interpretation remains extremely difficult, especially when alternative pathways may exist. Furthermore, many of the factors involved in the determination of steady state concentrations of these metabolites in either tissue or cerebrospinal fluid remain unknown.

The above methods for measurement of monoamine turnover have been applied in a number of experimental conditions. Some of the data obtained from various investigators is illustrated in Table 5-4. Pargyline, a monoamine oxidase inhibitor which causes an accumulation of monoamines within the brain,

TABLE 5.4. Effect of Various Procedures on Norepinephrine Turnover in Rat Brain

| Condition | Brain Region | T ½ (hr) | Turnover Rate μg/gm/hr |
|---|---|---|---|
| control | brain stem | 5.4 | 0.094 |
| pargyline | | 15.9 | 0.052 |
| control | brain stem + mesencephalon | 2.6 | 0.109 |
| electroconvulsive shock treatment | brain stem + mesencephalon | 2.3 | 0.152 |
| control | brain stem + mesencephalon | 2.6 | 0.148 |
| paradoxical sleep rebound | brain stem + mesencephalon | 1.5 | 0.270 |
| control (24°C) | hypothalamus | 5.09 | |
| | brain less hypothalamus | 2.72 | |
| high temp. (32°C) | hypothalamus | 1.77 | |
| | brain less hypothalamus | 2.18 | |
| low temp. (9°C) | hypothalamus | 5.78 | |
| | brain less hypothalamus | 2.91 | |

Data taken from Figs. 4 and 5, p. 53, L. L. Iversen and M. A. Simmonds, in: *Metabolism of Amines in the Brain*. (Ed. G. Hooper), Macmillan, 1969.

leads to a significant reduction in the turnover of norepinephrine. Electroconvulsive shock treatment and paradoxical sleep rebound lead to an increase in the turnover of brain stem + mesencephalic norepinephrine. Exposure of rats to a high environmental temperature (32° C) which causes about a 3° rise in rectal temperature produces a three-fold increase in the turnover of norepinephrine in the rat hypothalamus while it

TABLE 5-5. Turnover Time of Monoamine Stores of Various
Rat and Rabbit Tissue

| Animal Species | Tissue | Turnover Time (in hours) | Synthesis Rate μg/gm/hr |
|---|---|---|---|
| Rat | heart NE | 14.3 | 0.05 |
| | brain NE | 8.3 | 0.05 |
| | brain DA | 3.6 | 0.21 |
| | brain 5-HT | 1.2 | 0.50 |
| Rabbit | caudate DA | 3.0 | 2.85 |
| | hypothalamic NE | 5.3 | 0.46 |
| | midbrain NE | 5.0 | 0.12 |
| | superior cervical ganglion NE | 2.1 | 1.53 |
| | iris NE | 14.9 | 0.22 |
| | salivary gland NE | 10.0 | 0.12 |

Data taken from Table I and Table II in E. Costa and N. H. Neff, in
Proc. 3rd Int. Pharmacol. Meeting, 10, 15, 1968 Pergamon; and N. H.
Neff, and T. N. Tozer, Adv. Pharmacol., 6A, 97, 1968.

has no significant effect on the rest of the brain. Lowering
the environmental temperature, however, fails to cause a
change in the turnover of hypothalamic norepinephrine. Table 5-5 summarizes the turnover times of monoamine pools
found in various tissues of the rat and rabbit.

## Storage

A great conceptual advance made in the study of catecholamines in the past fifteen years was the recognition that in almost
all tissues a large percentage of the norepinephrine present is located within highly specialized subcellular particles (colloquially
referred to as "granules") in sympathetic nerve endings and chromaffin cells. Much of the norepinephrine in the central nervous

system is also presumably located within similar particles. These granules contain adenosine triphosphate (ATP) in a molar ratio of catecholamine to ATP of about 4 : 1. Because of this perhaps fortuitous ratio, it is generally supposed that the anionic phosphate groups of ATP form a salt link with norepinephrine, which exists as a cation at physiological pH, and thereby serve as a means to bind the amines within the vesicles. Some such complex of the amines with ATP, with ATP associated with protein, or with protein directly is probable since the intravesicular concentration of amines, at least in the adrenal chromaffin granules and probably also in the splenic nerve granules (0.3 to 1.1 M), would be hypertonic if present in free solution and might be expected to lead to osmotic lysis of the vesicles.

The catecholamine storage vesicles in adrenal chromaffin and splenic nerve appear to have a number of general properties:

a. they possess an outer limiting membrane;
b. with appropriate fixation they possess an electron dense core when viewed in the electron microscope;
c. they contain the enzyme dopamine-$\beta$-hydroxylase;
d. they have a high concentration of catecholamine and ATP in a 4 : 1 ratio;
e. chromaffin and splenic nerve granules contain a characteristic soluble protein (chromogranin) also suggested to be involved in the storage process;
f. they contain $Mg^{++}$ and $Ca^{++}$-dependent ATPase.

The various types of vesicles found in neural tissue or chromaffin cells are summarized in Figure 5-11, which indicates their approximate size and distribution. A number of possible functions which have been proposed for the catecholamine storage vesicles are summarized below:

a. They bind and store norepinephrine, thereby retarding its diffusion out of the neuron, and protect it from being destroyed by monoamine oxidase (MAO), which is considered to be intraneuronal;
b. they serve as a depot of transmitter which may be released upon the appropriate physiological stimulus;

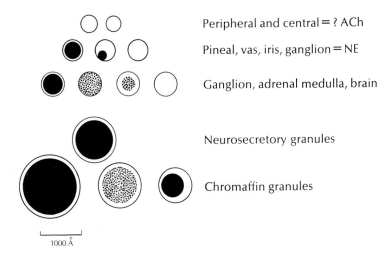

FIGURE 5-11. Size and electron microscopic appearance of the various types of synaptic vesicles, large granular vesicles, chromaffin granules, and neurosecretory granules found in various portions of the central and peripheral nervous system.

    c. they oxidize dopamine to norepinephrine;

    d. they take up dopamine from the cytoplasm, protecting it from oxidation by monoamine oxidase.

It is generally believed that the vesicles are formed in the neuronal cell body and subsequently transported to the nerve terminal region. This assumption is based upon a number of findings:

    a. only a minimal amount of protein biosynthesis occurs in axons or nerve terminals;

    b. following the depletion of norepinephrine by reserpine the amines first reappear within the perinuclear cytoplasm of the cell body;

    c. when the axon of a sympathetic nerve is constricted, structures (mainly large granular vesicles containing norepinephrine) tend to accumulate at the proximal border.

## Release

Much of the current knowledge regarding the release of catecholamines derives from the study of both adrenal medullary tissue and adrenergically innervated peripheral organs. Here it can be directly demonstrated that norepinephrine is released from the nerve terminals during periods of nerve stimulation and further that adrenergic fibers can sustain this output of transmitter during prolonged periods of stimulation, if synthesis and re-uptake of the transmitter are not impaired. In the periphery it is possible to isolate the innervated end-organs, to collect a perfusate from the vascular system during nerve stimulation, and to analyze this for the presence and quantity of a given putative transmitter. However, we really know little of the mechanism by which axonal nerve impulses arriving at the terminal cause the release of norepinephrine (excitation-secretion coupling). Our best appreciation of the events comes from the possible analogous release of catecholamines from the adrenal medulla, which has been extensively studied. For a comprehensive review of this area the reader is referred to Douglas (1968). The mechanism of catecholamine release by the adrenal medulla is thought to take place as follows: with activity in the preganglionic fibers, acetylcholine is released and thought to combine with the plasma membrane of the chromaffin cells. This produces a change in membrane protein conformation altering the permeability of this membrane to $Ca^{++}$ and other ions, which then move inward. The influx of $Ca^{++}$ is believed to be the main stimulus responsible for the mobilization of the catecholamines and for their secretion. The current view is that the catecholamines are released from the chromaffin cell by a process of exocytosis, along with chromogranin, ATP, and a little dopamine-$\beta$-hydroxylase. Whether or not these cellular phenomena are applicable to the sympathetic nerve endings in general remains to be determined.

Teleologically, it appears rather unlikely that transmitter release from sympathetic nerve terminals does occur exclusively by a process of exocytosis. Exocytosis requires that the entire content of the granular vesicle be released (that is, catecholamine, ATP, and soluble protein). Since the nerve terminal region, as far as we know now, cannot sustain any sort of protein biosynthesis, high rates of axonal flow from the nerve cell body would be required to replenish the protein lost during the process of exocytosis. Alternatively, one might propose a "protein re-uptake" mechanism in order to recapture that protein released during the process of synaptic transmission. In peripheral nerve, release of norepinephrine has been shown to be frequency dependent within a physiological range of frequency. This release of norepinephrine, similar to the release of ACh, is $Ca^{++}$-dependent. Some evidence has also been presented which indicates that newly synthesized norepinephrine may be released preferentially. This preferential release is additional evidence to support the contention that norepinephrine exists in more than one pool within the sympathetic neuron.

It has been a great deal more difficult to demonstrate release of a putative transmitter from a given type of nerve ending in the central nervous system. Thus it is impossible to perfuse specific localized brain areas through their vascular system. In addition, it is also difficult but not necessarily impossible to selectively stimulate a well-defined neuronal pathway within the brain (see Chapter 6). However, with the independent development of the push-pull cannula and the chemitrode, it has become possible to collect catecholamines from certain deep nuclear masses of the central nervous system. In addition, cortical cups, ventricular perfusions, brain slices, and isolated spinal cords have been used to demonstrate release of putative transmitters, including norepinephrine and dopamine from central nervous system tissue. All of these physiological techniques for studying release have some disadvantages and limitations and are somewhat gross and indirect (see Chapters 2 and 3). Nevertheless they do represent increasing sophistication in research on release occurring in the central nervous system.

*Metabolism*

The metabolism of exogenously administered or endogenous catecholamines differs markedly from that of acetylcholine in that the speed of degradation of the amines is considerably slower

Aldehyde Dehydrogenase

sulfate conjugate

$CH_3O$ ... $CH-CH_2OH$ / $HO$

MOPEG

$CH_3O$ ... $CH-COOH$ / $HO$ — VMA

COMT

$CH_3O$ ... $CH_2-CHO$ / $HO$

3-methoxy-4-hydroxyphenylglycolaldehyde

$HO$ ... $CH-CH_2OH$ / $HO$

DOPEG

COMT

MAO

Aldehyde Reductase

$CH_3O$ ... $CH-CH_2-NH_2$ / $HO$

NM

$HO$ ... $CH-CHO$ / $HO$

3,4-dihydroxyphenylglycolaldehyde

Aldehyde Dehydrogenase

$HO$ ... $CH-COOH$ / $HO$

DOMA

COMT

MAO

Tyrosine → DOPA → DA → NE

MAO     COMT

$HO$ ... $CH_2COOH$ / $HO$

DOPAC

Aldehyde Dehydrogenase

$HO$ ... $CH_2CHO$ / $HO$

3,4-dihydroxyphenylacetaldehyde

$CH_3O$ ... $CH_2-CH_2-NH_2$ / $HO$

MTA

MAO

$HO$ ... $CH_2CH_2OH$ / $HO$

DOPET

$CH_3O$ ... $CH_2CHO$ / $HO$

3-methoxy-4-hydroxyphenylacetaldehyde

COMT

Aldehyde Reductase

$CH_3O$ ... $CH_2CH_2OH$ / $HO$

3-methoxy-4-hydroxyphenylethanol

Aldehyde Dehydrogenase

$CH_3O$ ... $CH_2COOH$ / $HO$

HVA

than that of the ACh-ACh-esterase system. The major mammalian enzymes of importance in the metabolic degradation of catecholamines are monoamine oxidase and catechol-$O$-methyltransferase (COMT) (Fig. 5-12). Monoamine oxidase is an enzyme which converts catecholamines to their corresponding aldehydes. This

FIGURE 5-12. Dopamine and Norepinephrine Metabolism. The following abbreviations are used: DOPA, dihydroxyphenylalanine; DA, dopamine; NE, norepinephrine; DOMA, 3,4-dihydroxymandelic acid; DOPAC, 3,4-dihydroxyphenylacetic acid; DOPEG, 3,4-dihydroxyphenylglycol; DOPET, 3,4-dihydroxyphenylethanol; MOPET, 3-methoxy-4-hydroxy-phenylethanol; MOPEG, 3-methoxy-4-hydroxy-phenylglycol; HVA, homovanillic acid; VMA, 3-methoxy-4-hydroxy-mandelic acid; NM, normetanephrine; MTA, 3-methoxytyramine; MAO, monoamine oxidase; COMT, catechol-O-methyltransferase; Dashed arrows indicated steps which have not been firmly established.

aldehyde intermediate is rapidly metabolized, usually by oxidation by the enzyme aldehyde dehydrogenase to the corresponding acid. In some circumstances, the aldehyde is reduced to the alcohol or glycol by aldehyde reductase. In the case of central norepinephrine, reduction of the aldehyde metabolite appears to be the favored route of metabolism. Neither of these latter enzymes has been extensively studied in neuronal tissue. Monoamine oxidase is a particle-bound protein, localized largely in the outer membrane of mitochondria, although a partial microsomal localization cannot be excluded. There is also some evidence for a riboflavin-like material in monoamine oxidase from liver mitochondria. Monoamine oxidase is usually considered to be an intraneuronal enzyme, but it occurs in abundance extraneuronally. In fact, most experiments indicate that chronic denervation of a sympathetic end-organ leads only to a relatively small reduction in monoamine oxidase, suggesting that the greater proportion of this enzyme is, in fact, extraneuronal. However, it is the intraneuronal enzyme which seems to be important in catecholamine metabolism. Dopamine appears to be a better substrate for monoamine oxidase than either epinephrine or norepinephrine, and large amounts of the deaminated metabolites of dopamine (dihydroxyphenylacetic acid and homovanillic acid) are excreted daily in human urine. It has been speculated that under certain circumstances this enzyme could serve to regulate norepinephrine biosynthesis by controlling the amount of substrate, dopamine, available to the enzyme dopamine-$\beta$-hydroxylase. Monoamine oxidase is not an exclusive catabolic enzyme for the catecholamines since it also oxidatively deaminates other biogenic amines such as 5-hydroxytryptamine, tryptamine, and tyramine. The intraneuronal localization of monoamine oxidase in mitochondria or other structures suggests that this would limit its action to amines that are present in a free (unbound) form in the axoplasm. Here, monoamine oxidase can act on amines that have been taken up by the axon before they are granule-bound, or it can even act on amines that are released from the granules before they pass out through the axonal membrane. Interestingly, the latter possibility seems physiologically minor, since monoamine oxidase inhibition does not potentiate the effects of nerve stimulation.

The second enzyme of importance in the catabolism of catecholamines is catechol-O-methyltransferase discovered by Axelrod in 1957. This enzyme is a relatively nonspecific enzyme which catalyzes the transfer of methyl groups from S-adenosyl methionine to the m-hydroxyl group of catecholamines and various other catechol compounds. Catechol-O-methyltransferase is found in the cytoplasm of most animal tissue, being particularly abundant in kidney and liver. A substantial amount of this enzyme is also found in the central nervous system and in various sympathetically innervated organs. The precise cellular localization of catechol-O-methyltransferase has not been determined although it has been suggested (with little foundation) to function extraneuronally. The purified enzyme requires S-adenosyl methionine and $Mg^{++}$ ions for activity. As with monoamine oxidase, inhibition of catechol-O-methyltransferase activity does not markedly potentiate the effects of sympathetic nerve stimulation, although in some tissue it tends to prolong the response. Therefore, neither monoamine oxidase nor catechol-O-methyltransferase would seem to be the primary mechanism for terminating the action of norepinephrine liberated at sympathetic nerve terminals.

*Uptake*

When sympathetic postganglionic nerves are stimulated at frequencies low enough to be comparable to those encountered process clearly has an exceptionally high affinity for norepineph-rine. In fact, the actual concentration ratios between exogenous norepinephrine accumulated within the sympathetic neurons and that present in the medium could approach 10,000 : 1.

This uptake process is a saturable membrane transport process dependent upon temperature and requiring energy. The stereo-chemically preferred substrate is L-norepinephrine; furthermore, norepinephrine is taken up more efficiently than its $N$-substituted derivatives. This process is sodium dependent and can be blocked by inhibition of $Na^+$, $K^+$-activated ATPase. In fact, most evidence suggests that catecholamine uptake is mediated by some sort of active membrane transport mechanism located in the axonal mem-brane of postganglionic sympathetic neurons.


AXONAL TRANSPORT

The early estimates by Weiss of the rate of axoplasmic transport based both on the rate of regeneration of axons and on nerve constriction experiments suggested that the total mass of axonal material is transported distally at a rate of approximately 1 mm/day. More recent studies employing the use of radioactive substances and autoradiography have evaluated the transport of individual components of the axoplasm. Numerous demonstra-tions indicate some proteins are transported at rates of approxi-mately 1 mm/day; but, in addition, a heterogeneity of transport rates of some axoplasmic constituents, ranging up to 10 cm/day and even up to 1 meter/day, have also been reported. Many of these experiments have been concerned with the axonal trans-port of catecholamines, as described by Dahlström and her col-leagues in Sweden. They found that ligated sympathetic nerves accumulate norepinephrine above the ligation indicating a prox-imo-distal transport of amine-containing particles from the nerve cell body. Not only was this accumulation studied biochemically but also histochemical fluorescence observations of the zone of constriction were made at different times after ligation. It was found that when a sympathetic axon is crushed or ligated, there is an almost immediate accumulation of norepinephrine on the cell body side of the ligature or crush. After 12 to 24 hours there is a marked accumulation of norepinephrine in the segment proximal to the crush, with only a weak or small accumulation in the distal segment. The increase in norepinephrine on the proximal side proceeds linearly up to about 48 hours, at which time it tends to level off. Pharmacological treatment with reserpine indicated that the accumulated norepinephrine is stored within the granules. From the content of norepinephrine in 1 cm segments of non-ligated axon and the rate of accumulation of norepinephrine in the 1 cm segment proximal to the ligature, the velocity of the transport of the norepinephrine-containing particles was calculated to be about 5 mm/hr in the rat, 10 mm/hr in the cat, and 2-3 mm/hr in the rabbit.

Dahlström also made tandem constrictions by using two ligatures and found that the accumulation of norepinephrine was considerably larger above the proximal ligation than above the distal ligation. In the part of the nerve between the two ligatures, the total norepinephrine did not exceed the amount in a normal unligated nerve segment of the identical length, suggesting that local synthesis was probably not responsibe for the accumulation normally observed. Other experiments conducted in the central nervous system have suggested that the transport rate in this tissue is about 0.5 mm/hr.

Even in view of these fairly rapid rates of transport of catecholamine storage granules it seems unlikely that this transport process serves to replace transmitter normally lost during nerve activity. More probably this transport serves to replace the granular protein structure which houses or binds the catecholamine, and turns over at a slower rate than that of the amines.

NEUROTRANSMITTER ROLE

On the basis of many experiments demonstrating that norepinephrine is synthesized and stored in sympathetic neurons, that it is released in significant quantities in response to sympathetic nerve stimulation, that it produces effector organ responses identical to those produced by sympathetic nerve stimulation, and that drugs which antagonize the action of exogenous norepinephrine also block the effect of sympathetic nerve stimulation of the organ in question, it has been accepted by most investigators that norepinephrine is in fact the sympathetic neurotransmitter in the mammalian peripheral sympathetic nervous system.

At the present time it is also well accepted that norepinephrine acts as a neurotransmitter in the central nervous system although the evidence is not nearly so compelling. As described in Chapter 2 the central nervous system obviously presents an immediate obstacle to cellular investigations, namely, one of inaccessibility. Not only is the central nervous system of mammals relatively inaccessible but it does not have the clear-cut focal synaptic regions found in the peripheral nervous system. The cell bodies, dendrites, and axons of central neurons are usually studded with synaptic boutons. This, of course, provides the investigator with a totally heterogeneous system of chemical and perhaps electrical inputs in close proximity to each other, making it difficult to evaluate events taking place at a particular type of nerve ending. A number of criteria, of course, must be fulfilled before it is possible to accept a putative transmitter candidate as a true neurotransmitter at a given synaptic junction. These criteria have been reviewed in Chapter 2. Many of the proposed criteria for neurotransmitters have been satisfactorily fulfilled by norepinephrine and dopamine in the mammalian central nervous system. The major difficulties in transmitter identification in the central nervous system have been in demonstrating the release of the transmitter and in comparing the postsynaptic effects of presynaptic nerve stimulation and those obtained upon application of the putative transmitter to the postsynaptic receptor. If one imposes the most stringent criteria for evaluating release, it is necessary to demonstrate that the putative transmitter is released into the diffusable volume of the synaptic cleft in response to stimulation and depolarization of a given nerve terminal. At present no micromethod has yet been devised by which it is possible to study release at this fine level of refinement in the central nervous system. If one is not so critical, release of monoamines from central nervous system tissue can be demonstrated by a number of experimental techniques. For example norepinephrine is released from brain slices by gross nonspecific electrical stimulation. It has also been shown that stimulation of an isolated spinal cord produces a release of some norepinephrine and 5-hydroxytryptamine into the media.

With even less stringent criteria for release, perfusion of the lateral ventricles of cats reveals detectable amounts of dopamine, norepinephrine, and their metabolites in the cerebrospinal fluid after periods of low level stimulation of certain specific brain areas. Here, however, we must assume that the putative transmitter released from certain nerve endings within the brain escapes the recapture process and diffuses through the brain substance proper to be detected eventually in the cerebrospinal fluid. More "refined" techniques such as push-pull cannulae and chemitrodes have also provided evidence for norepinephrine and dopamine release in both acute and chronically implanted animals. This latter release is also enhanced by electrical stimulation or by certain drugs. A number of indirect techniques have also been used to demonstrate release in vivo. Thus, fluorescence histochemical experiments demonstrating depletion of nerve terminal fluorescence have been used as an index of release. Similarly, biochemical studies demonstrating depletion of catecholamines have been used as an index of release. However, other plausible explanations of this depletion such as acceleration of catabolism should also be considered.

It has also been difficult in the central nervous system to demonstrate that administration of an exogenous quantity of a putative transmitter produces the same effect as nerve terminal depolarization and that drugs which block the action of this natural transmitter at the receptor also exhibit the same degree of sensitivity toward the putative transmitter. Microiontophoresis has provided a powerful tool toward this end.

By means of this technique these criteria have been satisfied for the cerebellum (see Chapter 9), the olfactory bulb and for the caudate nucleus. In the olfactory bulb norepinephrine may be a mediator of a recurrent inhibitory synaptic pathway since: (a) iontophoretically applied norepinephrine depresses spontaneous activity; (b) this effect as well as depression due to synaptic inhibition can be blocked by dibenamine, an $\alpha$-adrenergic blocking agent; (c) synaptic inhibition is reduced when catecholamines are depleted by pretreating animals with reserpine and $\alpha$-methyl tyrosine; (d) norepinephrine-containing nerve endings appear to be restricted to the layer in the olfactory bulb where synaptic inhibition is most easily demonstrated.

In the caudate nucleus and spinal cord, areas rich in catecholamine-containing nerve endings, $\alpha$-receptor blocking drugs are also capable of blocking the response to iontophoretically applied catecholamines. Further, in the caudate nucleus this response to the catecholamines is identical with that resulting from stimulation of the substantia nigra where dopamine-containing nerve endings are thought to arise. The effects of iontophoretically applied dopamine can also be blocked by chlorpromazine.

In almost all cases the response of single neurons to norepinephrine and dopamine is a depression of spontaneous activity. In the cerebellum the norepinephrine response appears to be mediated by cyclic AMP. (See Chapter 9.)

It is clear that a great deal of evidence favors the possibility that both norepinephrine and dopamine do play such a transmitter role in the central nervous system.

## PHARMACOLOGY OF CATECHOLAMINE NEURONS

In this section we will focus on the pharmacology of peripheral noradrenergic neurons discussing possible sites of drug involvement in the life cycle of the catecholamines. Figure 5-13 depicts a schematic model of a noreadrenergic nerve varicosity.

*Site-1—Precursor transport.* As noted earlier there appears to be an active uptake or transport of tyrosine as well as other aromatic amino acids into the central nervous system. In addition it is also probable that tyrosine is actively taken up by adrenergic

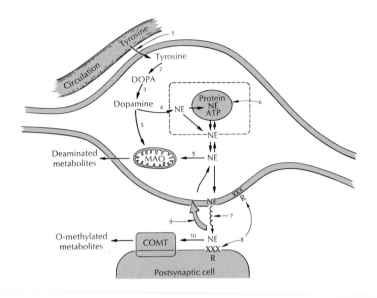

FIGURE 5-13. Schematic model of noradrenergic neuron.

neurons both in the periphery and in the central nervous system. At present we have no pharmacologic agent which specifically antagonizes the uptake of tyrosine into the brain or into the catecholamine-containing neuron. However, it is known that various aromatic amino acids will compete with each other for transport into the central nervous system. This competition might become important under a pathological situation in which blood aromatic amino acids are elevated. Thus in phenylketonuria, when plasma levels of phenylalanine are elevated to about $10^{-3}$M, it might be expected that tyrosine and tryptophan uptake into the brain might be diminished.

*Site-2—Tyrosine hydroxylase.* The conversion of tyrosine to DOPA is the rate limiting step in this biosynthetic pathway and thus is the step most susceptible to pharmacological manipulation. The various classes of tyrosine hydroxylase inhibitors were considered earlier in this chapter. α-Methyl-*p*-tyrosine, an effective inhibitor of tyrosine hydroxylase both *in vivo* and *in vitro*, is one of the few tyrosine hydroxylase inhibitors which has been employed clinically and found to be effective in the treatment of pheochromocytomas; it is of little or no value in the treatment of essential hypertension.

*Sites-3 and 4—DOPA-decarboxylase and dopamine-β-oxidase.* Potent inhibitors of DOPA-decarboxylase and dopamine-β-oxidase do exist but they are generally not effective *in vivo* in reducing tissue concentrations of catecholamines.

Due to the nonspecificity of these two enzymes (see above) as well as the relatively nonspecific vesicular storage sites, certain drugs or even amines or amine precursors in foodstuff can be synthesized to phenylethylamine derivatives with a catechol or a β-hydroxyl group and taken up and stored in the storage vesicles. These compounds can subsequently be released by sympathetic nerves, in part replacing some of the norepinephrine normally released by sympathetic impulses. Since these "false neurotransmitters" are less potent in their action, replacement of some of the endogenous, releasable pool of norepinephrine with these agents results in a diminished sympathetic response. Thus a drug such as α-methyldihydroxyphenylalanine, which is converted in the sympathetic neuron to α-methyl-norepinephrine, replaces a portion of the endogenous norepinephrine and itself can be subsequently released as a "false transmitter." The false transmitter theory also has been used to explain the hypotensive action of various monoamine oxidase inhibitors. Tyramine, an endogenous metabolite which is normally disposed of by monoamine oxidase in the liver and other tissues, is no longer rapidly deaminated in the presence of monoamine oxidase inhibitors and thus can be converted to the β-hydroxylated derivative octopamine which then accumulates in sympathetic neurons. Upon activation of these nerves, octopamine is released and acts as a false neurotransmitter, producing a resultant decrease in sympathetic tone (observed with monoamine oxidase inhibitors). "False neurotransmitters" can also be formed in the brain but at the present time the action of these agents is unclear.

*Site-5—Metabolic degradation by monoamine oxidase.* The monoamine oxidase inhibitors comprise quite a heterogeneous group of drugs which have in common the ability to block the oxidative deamination of various biogenic amines. These agents all produce marked increases in tissue amine concentrations. These compounds are in most cases employed clinically for the treatment of depression. However, some of these agents are used for the treatment of hypertension and angina pectoris. In the case of monoamine oxidase inhibitors, it should be immediately pointed out that while these drugs inhibit monoamine oxidase, there is no firmly established correlation between monoamine oxidase inhibition and therapeutic effect. In fact, it is generally well appreciated that monoamine oxidase inhibitors inhibit not only enzymes involved in oxidative deamination of monoamines but in addition many other enzymes unrelated to monoamine oxidase such as succinic dehydrogenase, dopamine $\beta$-oxidase, 5-hydroxy-tryptophan decarboxylase, choline dehydrogenase, and diamine oxidase.

*Site-6—Storage.* A number of drugs, most notably the Rauwolfia alkaloids, interfere with the storage of monoamines by blocking the uptake of amine into the storage granules or by disrupting the binding of the amines. Thus drugs interfering with the storage mechanism will cause amines to be released intraneuronally. Amines released intraneuronally appear to be preferentially metabolized by monoamine oxidase.

*Site-7—Release.* The release of catecholamines is dependent upon $Ca^{++}$ ions. Thus, in an *in vitro* system it is possible to block release by lowering the $Ca^{++}$ concentration of the medium. Although drugs such as bretylium act to inhibit the release of norepinephrine in the peripheral nervous system, this drug does not easily penetrate the brain and thus has little or no effect on central monoaminergic neurons.

*Site-8—Interaction with receptors.* $\alpha$ and $\beta$ adrenergic blocking agents are effective in the peripheral nervous system. These agents block both the effects of sympathetic nerve stimulation and the action of exogenously administered norepinephrine. Some of these agents also have central activity. Recent evidence has indicated that pre-synaptic-$\alpha$-receptors are involved in the regulation of norepinephrine release. A blockade of these receptors facilitates release while stimulation leads to an inhibition of release. *Site-9—Re-uptake.* Drugs such as cocaine, desipramine, amitryptyline, and other related tricyclic antidepressants are effective inhibitors of norepinephrine uptake both at peripheral and central sites. Pharmacological intervention at these sites makes more norepinephrine available to the receptor and thus tends to potentiate adrenergic transmission.

*Site-10—Catechol-O-methyltransferase.* Catechol-O-methyltransferase can be inhibited by pyrogallol or various tropolone derivatives. Inhibition of this enzyme in most sympathetically innervated tissue such as heart does not significantly potentiate the effects of nerve stimulation. In vascular tissue, however, inhibition of this enzyme does lead to a significant prolongation of the response to nerve stimulation. It appears possible that in this tissue catechol-O-methyltransferase may play some role in terminating transmitter action.

Axelrod, J. (1971). Noradrenaline: Fate and control of its biosynthesis. Science 173:598, 1971.

Bloom, F. E. (1970). The fine structural localization of biogenic monoamines in nervous tissue. International Rev. Neurobiology, 13: 27.

Bloom, F. E., and N. J. Giarman (1968). Current status of neurotransmitters. Ann. Rep. Medicinal Chem., Chap. 25, Academic Press, New York.

Costa, E. (1970). Simple neuronal models to estimate turnover rate of noradrenergic transmitters in vivo. Adv. Biochem. Psychopharmacology 2: 169.

Dahlström, A., and J. Häggendal (1970). Axonal Transport of Amine Storage Granules in Sympathetic Adrenergic Neurons. Adv. Biochem. Psychopharmacol. 2 65.

De Potter, W. P., Chubb, I. W. and De Schaepdryver. (1972). Pharmacological aspects of peripheral noradrenergic transmission. Arch. Int. Pharmacodyn. therap. suppl. 196: 258.

Douglas, W. W. (1968). Stimulus-secretion coupling: The concept and clues from chromaffin and other cells. Brit. J. Pharmacol. 34: 451.

Euler, U. S. von (1956). Noradrenaline. Charles C Thomas, Springfield, Ill.

Iversen, L. L. (1971). Role of transmitter uptake mechanisms in synaptic neurotransmission. Brit. J. Pharmacol. 41: 571.

Kopin, I. J. (1968). False adrenergic transmitters. Ann. Rev. Pharmacol. 8: 377.

Molinoff, P. B., and J. Axelrod (1971). Biochemistry of Catecholamines. Ann. Review Biochem. 40: 465.

Moore, K. E., and J. A. Dominic (1971). Tyrosine hydroxylase inhibitors. Fed. Proc. 30: 859.

Smith, A. D. (1972). Subcellular localization of noradrenaline in sympathetic neurons. Pharmacol. Rev. 24: 435.

Thoenen, H., and Tranzer, J. P. (1973). The pharmacology of 6-hydroxydopamine. Ann. Rev. Pharmacol. 13: 169.

Udenfriend, S. (1962). *Fluorescence Assay in Biology and Medicine*. Academic Press, New York.

Usdin, E., and S. H. Snyder (1973). Frontiers in catecholamine research. Proceedings of the Third International Catecholamine Symposium. Pergamon Press, New York.

Vane, J. R. (1969). The release and fate of vaso-active hormones in the circulation. Brit. J. Pharmacol. 35: 209.

Weiner, N. (1970). Regulation of norepinephrine biosynthesis. Ann. Rev. Pharmac. 10: 273.

Weil-Malherbe, H. (1971). The chemical estimation of catecholamines and their metabolites in body fluids and tissue extracts. In: *Methods of Biochemical Analysis*, Supplemental volume p. 119, D. Glick (ed.), Interscience Publishers, New York.

# 6 | Catecholamines II: CNS Aspects

THE CELLULAR ORGANIZATION of the brain and spinal cord has been studied for many decades by classical histological and silver impregnation techniques. With the development in the last decade of completely different histological techniques based on the presence of a given type of transmitter substance or on specific synthetic enzymes involved in the formation of a given transmitter, it has become possible to map chemically defined neuronal systems in the CNS. With the formaldehyde fluorescence histochemical method of Falck and Hillarp (see Chapter 5), it has been possible to delineate norepinephrine-, dopamine-, and 5-hydroxytryptamine-containing systems in mammalian brain. Even though such techniques have been employed for only a few years, it is already becoming clear that the distribution of these chemically defined neuronal systems does not necessarily correspond to that of systems described earlier with the classical techniques.

It was really not until the mid 1960's that the histochemical

---

FIGURE 6-1. Schematic illustration of a central monoamine containing neuron. The right side depicts the general appearance and intraneuronal distribution of monoamines based upon fluorescence microscopy. The cell bodies contain a relatively low concentration of catecholamine (about 10-100 $\mu$g/gm) while the terminal varicosities contain a very high concentration (1000 to 3000 $\mu$g/gm). The preterminal axons contain very low concentration of amine. At the electron microscopic level (left side) dense core granules can be observed in the cell bodies and axons but appear to be highly concentrated in the terminal varicosities. (Illustration adapted after K. Fuxe and T. Hökfelt, in *Triangle*, 30: 73, 1971.)

fluorescent technique was applied to brain tissue and the anatomy of the monoamine-containing neuronal systems was described. By a variety of pharmacological and chemical methods, it has subsequently been possible to discriminate between norepinephrine- and dopamine-containing neurons and to describe in detail the distribution of these catecholamine-containing neurons in the rat central nervous system. The most recent and thorough evaluation of these systems has been made by Ungerstedt.

Schematic diagram of Monoamine Neuron

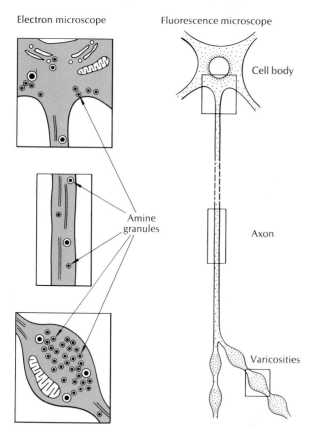

Figure 6-1 provides a schematic model of a central monoamine-containing neuron as observed by fluorescence and electron microscopy. The cell bodies contain relatively low concentrations of amine (about 10-100 μg/gm), while the terminal varicosities contain a very high concentration (about 1000 to 3000 μg/gm). The axons, on the other hand, consist of highly branched, largely unmyelinated fibers which have such a low concentration of amine that they are barely visible in untreated adult animals. With the electron microscope, depending on the type of fixation, it is possible to observe the presence of dense core granules which are thought to represent the subcellular storage sites containing the catecholamines (see Chapter 5). These granules, or dense core vesicles, appear to be concentrated in the terminal varicosities of the monoamine neuron.

The norepinephrine-containing neurons of the brain originate from cell bodies found in both the pons and medulla oblongata. These cell bodies give rise to the ascending pathways which have

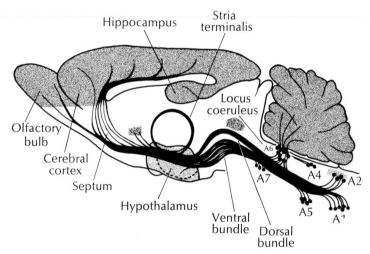

FIGURE 6-2. Schematic diagram illustrating the distribution of the main ascending central neuronal pathways containing norepinephrine. The stippled regions indicate the major nerve terminal areas. The cell groups are named according to the nomenclature of Dahlström and Fuxe (1965). (Modified after U. Ungerstedt, *Acta Physiol. Scand.* (1971) Suppl. 367.)

monosynaptic connections with the cortical areas, limbic system, and hypothalamus and the descending pathways which have monosynaptic connections with all parts of the spinal cord. The distribution of this monoamine system, as described in the rat, is illustrated in Figure 6-2.

One group of these norepinephrine neurons is particularly amenable to experimental investigation: the norepinephrine neurons originating in the locus coeruleus and responsible for in-

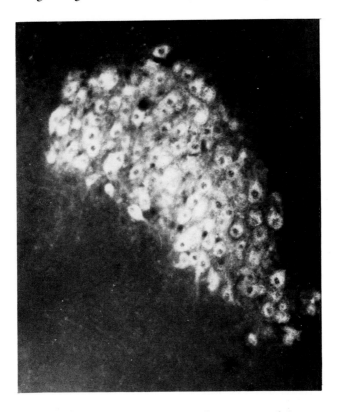

FIGURE 6-3. Formaldehyde-induced fluorescence of the rat nucleus locus coeruleus. In this frontal section through the principal portion of the nucleus, intensely fluorescent neurons can be seen clustered closely together. Within the neurons, the nucleus, which is not fluorescent after this treatment, appears dark except for the nucleolus. (Magnification 650x; Bloom, unpublished.)

nervating the cerebellar and cerebral cortex and the hippocampus. The compact nature of these norepinephrine cells, as seen in the locus coeruleus of the rat, is shown in Figure 6-3. It can be seen that the cells are tightly clustered together, almost resembling a sympathetic ganglion in the peripheral nervous system. Also, the projections are very diffuse, bearing a strong resemblance to the sympathetic nervous system in the periphery. In the rat locus coeruleus the noradrenergic cell bodies are so densely packed that they are probably the only neuronal type in this nucleus. Primarily because of the anatomical organization of this monoamine system in the brain, it is possible to make electrophysiological recordings from these neurons and selectively to stimulate or destroy them by chemical or mechanical means.

Despite the compactness of the cell bodies of the noradrenergic neuronal system, the terminal networks of this system are quite diffuse, as we have already mentioned. In the dopamine system it has been estimated that each monoamine-containing cell body

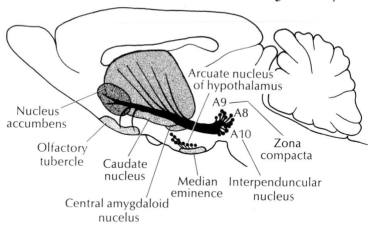

FIGURE 6-4. Schematic diagram indicating the distribution of the main central neuronal pathways containing dopamine. The stippled regions indicate the major nerve terminal areas. The cell groups are named according to the nomenclature of Dahlström and Fuxe (1965). (Modified after U. Ungerstedt, *Acta Physiol. Scand.* (1971) Suppl. 367.)

gives rise to approximately 500,000 terminals. The fact th
adrenergic cells also give rise to large collateral networks c
innervating many brain areas provides the morphological b
a neuronal system that influences activity in a very wide
area of the brain. It has been shown, for example, that in th
of norepinephrine-containing neurons in the locus coerule
cell body sends tracts to both the cerebral cortex and the c
lum. Because of the diffuseness of these noradrenergic syst
seems quite likely that their functions could be related to m
tion of various states or moods.

In contrast to the norepinephrine system, the dopamine sy
has a somewhat more restricted innervation. Anatomically, t
are three well-defined dopamine systems in the rat brain (see
6-4). Cell bodies of nigrostriatal dopamine system are located
marily in the zona compact of the substantia nigra (Fig. 6-5),

FIGURE 6-5. Fluorescence micrograph illustrating the fluorescent
dopamine cells found in the zona compacta of the rat. Scale:
0.1mm, abbreviation: ZR—zona reticulate. (From Bunney *et al.*,
1973.)

these neurons project mainly to the neostriatum and the central portion of the amygdaloid nucleus. Cell bodies of the mesolimbic dopamine system are located just dorsal to the interpeduncular nucleus in the ventral tegmental area, and these cells innervate the nucleus accumbens and olfactory tubercles. Cell bodies of the tuberoinfundibular dopamine system are found primarily in the arcuate nucleus of the hypothalamus and these cells mainly innervate the external layer of the median eminence. The dopamine neurons in this last system seem to behave differently from those found in the nigrostriatal or mesolimbic system. The tuberoinfundibular dopamine system is insensitive to the normal destructive actions of 6-hydroxydopamine and when activated for any length of time the terminals become markedly depleted of transmitter. It almost appears that the neurons in this system behave in a manner similar to that of classical neurosecretory neurons.

Norepinephrine neurons seem to be involved in many generalized CNS functions such as sleep and wakefulness, emotion, neuroendocrine function, and perhaps temperature regulation. The dopamine neuronal systems tend to be somewhat more discrete in their localization, and in some cases have a more clearly defined function. The nigro-neostriatal dopamine system appears to be largely involved in motor function while the tuberoinfundibular dopamine neurons are involved primarily in hypothalamic-pituitary control, probably *via* the release of luteinizing hormone releasing factor. The function of the mesolimbic dopamine system is at present unknown, although it is conceivable that it might play some role in mental function.

## Catecholamine Metabolism

Catecholamine metabolism has been dealt with in detail in Chapter 5 and only a few aspects pertinent to central catecholamine metabolism will be covered here.

In the peripheral sympathetic nervous system the aldehyde intermediate produced by the action of MAO on norepinephrine and normetanephrine can be oxidized to the corresponding acid

or reduced to the corresponding glycol. Oxidation usually exceeds reduction and quantitatively vanilylmandelic acid (VMA) is the major metabolite of norepinephrine and is readily detectable in the urine. In fact, the urinary levels of VMA are routinely measured in clinical laboratories in order to provide an index of peripheral sympathetic nerve function as well as to diagnose the presence of catecholamine-secreting tumors such as pheochromocytomas and neuroblastomas. In the central nervous system, however, reduction of the intermediate aldehyde formed by the action of MAO on catecholamines or catecholamine metabolites predominates, and a major metabolite of norepinephrine found in brain is the glycol derivative, 3-methoxy-4-hydroxy-phenethyleneglycol (MHPG). Very little if any VMA is found in brain. In many species a large fraction of the MHPG formed in brain is sulfate conjugated. Some normetanephrine is also found in the brain and spinal cord. Destruction of noradrenergic neurons in the brain or spinal cord cause a marked reduction of these metabolites. Recently, it has been demonstrated that direct electrical stimulation of the locus coeruleus or severe stress produces an increase in the turnover of norepinephrine as well as an increase in the accumulation of the sulfate conjugate of MHPG in the rat cerebral cortex. These effects are completely abolished by ablation of the locus coeruleus, suggesting that the accumulation of MHPG-sulfate in brain may reflect the functional activity of central noradrenergic neurons. Since MHPG-sulfate readily diffuses from the brain into the CSF or general circulation, estimates of its concentration in the CSF or in urine are thought to provide a possible reflection of activity of noradrenergic neurons in the brain. Even though MHPG is proportionately a minor metabolite of norepinephrine in the peripheral sympathetic nervous system, a large portion of the MHPG in the urine still derives from the periphery and only a minor contribution is made by brain (20 to 30 per cent). Thus, it is quite probable that relatively large changes in the formation of MHPG by brain are necessary to produce detectable changes in urinary MHPG. This certainly appears to be the case in the rat where destruction of the majority of norepinephrine-containing neurons in the brain by treatment with 6-hydroxy-dopamine leads to only about a 25 per cent decrease in urinary MHPG levels. Nevertheless, measurement of urinary changes in MHPG is still a reasonable strategy for obtaining some insight into possible alterations of central norepinephrine metabolism in patients with psychiatric illnesses. Measurement of CSF levels of MHPG and its sulfate conjugate also provide another possible approach to assessing central adrenergic function in human subjects. Although changes in either urinary or CSF levels of MHPG and their relationship to central noradrenergic function have to be interpreted with considerable caution, these measurements do provide a starting point for clinical investigation.

The primary metabolites of dopamine found in the CNS are homovanillic acid (HVA) and dihydroxyphenylacetic acid (DOPAC) and a small amount of 3-methoxytyramine. Thus, in this system the acidic rather than the neutral metabolites appear to predominate. Accumulation of HVA in brain or CSF has often been used to provide an index of the functional activity of dopaminergic neurons in the brain. Drugs such as the antipsychotic drugs which increase the turnover of dopamine, due in part to their ability to increase the activity of dopaminergic neurons, also increase the amount of HVA in the brain and CSF. In addition, electrical stimulation of the nigrostriatal pathway causes an increase in the release of HVA into ventricular perfusates. In disease states such as Parkinsonism, where there are degenerative changes in the substantia nigra and partial destruction of the dopamine neurons, a reduction of HVA is observed in the CSF.

Recently, it has been demonstrated that in rat brain the short-term accumulation of DOPAC in the striatum may provide an even more accurate reflection of activity in dopaminergic neurons of the nigrostriatal pathway. A cessation of impulse flow induced by placement of acute lesions in the nigrostriatal pathway leads to a rapid decrease in striatal DOPAC, and electrical stimulation of the nigrostriatal pathway results in a frequency-dependent increase in DOPAC within the striatum. Drugs such as the antipsychotic phenothiazines and butyrophenones, as well as anesthetics and hypnotics, which increase impulse flow in the nigrostriatal pathway also increase DOPAC. Drugs which block impulse flow such as γ-hydroxybutyrate and amphetamine cause a reduction in DOPAC. Thus, there appears to be an excellent correlation between changes in impulse flow in dopaminergic neurons induced either pharmacologically or mechanically and changes in the steady state levels of DOPAC. However, it has been difficult to measure DOPAC levels in the CSF of animals and humans so at the present time the question whether or not changes in CSF levels of this metabolite will reflect changes in the activity of dopamine neurons remains unanswered.

### BIOCHEMICAL ORGANIZATION

In general, noradrenergic neurons in the central nervous system appear to behave in a fashion quite similar to the postganglionic sympathetic noradrenergic neurons in the periphery. Electrical stimulation of the noradrenergic neurons in the locus coeruleus causes both an increase in the turnover of norepinephrine as well as a frequency-dependent accumulation of MHPG-sulfate (a major metabolite of norepinephrine in the rat CNS) in the cortex. Interruption of impulse flow in these neurons decreases turnover of norepinephrine but has little or no effect on the steady state level of transmitter. Similar effects are also obtained in the serotonin-containing neurons of the midbrain raphe (stimulation increasing synthesis and turnover, and interruption of impulse flow slowing turnover).

It is well known that acute stress also causes an increase in the turnover of norepinephrine in the CNS, which is believed to occur as a result of increase in impulse flow in noradrenergic neurons. Recent experiments have confirmed this speculation. If impulse flow in noradrenergic neurons projecting to the cortex is acutely interrupted by destruction of the locus coeruleus, the increase in norepinephrine turnover and accumulation of MHPG-sulfate induced by stress is completely blocked.

Dopaminergic neurons in the CNS do not behave in a fashion

completely analogous to peripheral or central noradrenergic neurons. An increase in impulse flow in the nigro-neostriatal or mesolimbic dopamine system does lead to both an increase in dopamine synthesis and turnover and a frequency-dependent increase in the accumulation of dopamine metabolites in the striatum and olfactory tubercle. These observations are similar to those made in other monoamine systems where an increase in impulse flow causes an increase in the synthesis and turnover of transmitter. However, if impulse flow is interrupted in the nigro-neostriatal or mesolimbic dopamine system either mechanically or pharmacologically by treatment with γ-hydroxybutyrate, the neurons respond in a rather peculiar fashion by rapidly increasing the concentration of dopamine in the nerve terminals of the respective dopamine systems. Not only do the terminals accumulate dopamine but there is also a dramatic increase in the rate of dopamine synthesis despite the steadily increasing concentration of endogenous dopamine within the nerve terminals.

Numerous regulatory mechanisms have been proposed to explain the way monoaminergic neurons control the synthesis of their neurotransmitters. In the case of the catecholamines, feedback inhibition of the rate-limiting enzyme, tyrosine hydroxylase, by the products dihydroxyphenylalanine, dopamine, and norepinephrine has been suggested as playing a primary role. The finding that interruption of impulse flow in dopamine-containing neurons appears to lead to an activation of dopamine synthesis seems at first glance to be inconsistent with this hypothesis. Since the actual concentration of dopamine in the dopaminergic terminals in the striatum dramatically increases, one would predict that this change should lead to a decrease in tyrosine hydroxylase activity, provided that the dopamine is accessible to tyrosine hydroxylase. Most recent experiments tend to suggest, however, that new dopamine formed under these conditions may be in a bound form and therefore inaccessible to tyrosine hydroxylase. If endogenous levels of dopamine are increased by other means such as administration of monoamine oxidase inhibitors, which tend to cause a greater increase in "free" soluble dopamine, a marked inhibition of synthesis is observed. Since it is reasonable to believe that interruption of impulse flow leads to a diminished release of dopamine into the synaptic cleft and to a depletion of dopamine at receptor sites, both pre- and postsynaptic, it seems possible that this lack of receptor activation could be the triggering mechanism which leads to some sort of feedback activation of tyrosine hydroxylase and the dramatic increase in synthesis.

Regardless of the mechanisms involved, it is quite clear that an inhibition of impulse flow in dopaminergic neurons leads to a marked increase in dopamine synthesis. This observation thus cautions against the use of turnover measures involving the administration of labeled tyrosine to assess functional activity of dopamine neurons since both an increase and an inhibition of impulse flow in this neuronal system will give the same biochemical results (i.e. an increase in the rate of accumulation of labeled dopamine from precursor tyrosine).

From the discussion above it should be apparent that the identification of specific chemically-defined neuronal systems in the brain sets the stage for investigation of the functional organization of these systems as well as for integrating biochemical and neurophysiological knowledge of the mechanism of action of drugs. Some specific examples of the effects of drugs on the activity of noradrenergic and dopaminergic neurons will be given in the section following.

PHARMACOLOGY OF CENTRAL CATECHOLAMINE-CONTAINING NEURONS

The psychotropic drugs (drugs which alter behavior, mood, and perception in man and behavior in animals) can be divided into two main categories, the psychotherapeutic drugs and the psychotomimetic agents. The psychotherapeutic drugs can be further divided on the basis of their activity in man into at least four general classes: antipsychotics, antianxiety drugs, antidepressants, and stimulants.

*Antipsychotic Drugs (major tranquilizers)*

Although there are seven major classes of antipsychotic drugs, all of which have in common the ability to ameliorate psychosis and evoke extrapyramidal reactions, those used currently are the phenothiazines, thioxanthenes, and butyrophenones. As might be expected from the name given to chlorpromazine by the French—Largactil—the phenothiazines are notorious for their wide spectrum of pharmacological and biochemical effects. Fortunately, however, it turns out that many actions attributable to the antipsychotic phenothiazines are non-specific properties of the phenothiazine moiety itself and do not appear to be correlated with the antipsychotic potency of this subgroup of phenothiazines. Along with many of their other actions, the antipsychotic phenothiazines have been shown to interact with both noradrenergic and dopaminergic neurons. However, the antipsychotic potency of these compounds appears to be best correlated with their ability to interact with dopamine-containing neurons. Much evidence has accumulated which indicates that antipsychotic drugs are effective blockers of dopamine receptors. In fact, it is believed that this reduction in dopamine activity expressed postsynaptically is responsible for the extrapyramidal side effects observed with these drugs. The ability of antipsychotic phenothiazines to block dopamine receptors on as yet chemically unidentified postsynaptic neurons may in some way also be related to the antipsychotic potency of these agents.

For many years it has been appreciated that antipsychotic drugs of both the phenothiazine and butyrophenone classes can cause an increase in the turnover of dopamine in the CNS. Since these drugs appear to have potent dopamine receptor blocking capabilities, it has been suggested that the increase observed in dopamine turnover results from a feedback activation of the dopaminergic neurons, presumably by some sort of neuronal feedback loop. This speculation has recently been verified by direct extracellular recording techniques (see below).

*Antianxiety Drugs (minor tranquilizers)*

The antianxiety drugs appear to interact primarily with noradrenergic neurons. They can create a very effective blockade of the stress-induced increase in the turnover of norepinephrine. The actual mechanism by which these drugs exert their effects on the norepinephrine systems is at the present time unknown. However, it may at least be speculated that in man the relief of stress symptoms is perhaps mediated by "turning off" the central noradrenergic neurons.

*Antidepressants*

There are two major classes of antidepressant drugs, the monoamine oxidase inhibitors (MAOI) and the tricyclics. The MAOI's interact with both noradrenergic and dopaminergic neurons. By definition these agents inhibit the enzyme MAO which is involved in oxidatively deaminating catecholamines, and thus cause an increase in the endogenous levels of both dopamine and norepinephrine in the brain. At least from a biochemical standpoint, the tricyclic antidepressants appear to interact primarily with noradrenergic rather than dopaminergic neurons. The secondary amine derivatives such as desipramine are exceptionally potent inhibitors of norepinephrine uptake but have only a minimal effect on dopamine uptake. The tertiary amine derivatives are less effective in inhibiting norepinephrine uptake but are very effective in blocking serotonin uptake.

*Stimulants*

The therapeutic usage of this class of drugs is becoming less and less common as awareness of their abuse potential increases. At the present time, in fact, their use is largely restricted to the treatment of narcolepsy and hyperkinetic children. The principal drugs in this category are the various analogues and isomers of amphetamine and methylphenidate.

For many years it has been known that ingestion of large amounts of amphetamine often leads to a state of paranoid psychosis that may be hard to distinguish from the paranoia associated with schizophrenia. It now appears that this paranoid state can be readily and reproducibly induced in human volunteers given large amounts of amphetamine so that the drug may provide a convenient "model psychosis" for experimental study. It is of interest in this regard that antipsychotic drugs such as chlorpromazine can readily reverse the amphetamine-induced psychosis.

On a biochemical level it was no surprise to learn that amphetamine and related compounds interact with catecholamine-containing neurons, since amphetamine is a close structural analogue of the catecholamines. However, there was no clear evidence that amphetamine produced its CNS effects through a catechol-

FIGURE 6-6. Schematic model of central noradrenergic neuron indicating possible sites of drug action.

Step 1: Enzymatic synthesis:

    a. Tyrosine hydroxylase reaction blocked by the competitive inhibitor, α-methyltyrosine.

    b. Dopamine-β-hydroxylase reaction blocked by a dithio-carbamate derivative, Fla-63 bis-(1-methyl-4-homopiperazinyl-thiocarbonyl)-disulfide.

Step 2: Storage. Reserpine and tetrabenazine interfere with the uptake-storage mechanism of the amine granules. The depletion of norepinephrine produced by reserpine is long-lasting and the storage granules are irreversibly damaged. Tetrabenazine also interferes with the uptake-storage mechanism of the granules except the effects of this drug do not appear to be irreversible.

Step 3: Release. Amphetamine appears to cause an increase in the net release of norepinephrine. Probably the primary mechanism by which amphetamine causes release is by its ability to block effectively the re-uptake mechanism.

Step 4: Receptor interaction: Clonidine appears to be a very potent receptor stimulating drug. Phenoxybenzamine and phentolamine are effective alpha receptor blocking agents. Recent experiments indicated that these drugs may also have presynaptic site of action.

Step 5: Reuptake: Norepinephrine has its action terminated by being taken up into the presynaptic terminal. The tricyclic drug, desipramine is a potent inhibitor of this uptake mechanism.

Step 6: Monoamine Oxidase (MAO): Norepinephrine or dopamine present in a free state within the presynaptic terminal can be degraded by the enzyme MAO which appears to be located in the outer membrane of mitochondria. Pargyline is an effective inhibitor of MAO.

Step 7: Catechol-O-methyltransferase (COMT): Norepinephrine can be inactivated by the enzyme COMT, which is believed to be localized outside the presynaptic neuron. Tropolone is an inhibitor of COMT. The normetanephrine (NM) formed by the action of COMT on NE can be further metabolized by MAO and aldehyde reductase to 3-methoxy-4-hydroxyphenylglycol (MHPG). The MHPG formed can be further metabolized to MHPG-sulfate by the action of a sulfotransferase found in brain.

amine mechanism until it was demonstrated that α-methyl-*p*-tyrosine (a potent inhibitor of tyrosine hydroxylase) prevented most of the behavioral effects of d-amphetamine. The question as to which catecholamine, norepinephrine or dopamine, is involved in the behavioral effects of amphetamine is still an open question. But, it is generally believed that the so-called stereotypic behavior in animals (i.e. compulsive gnawing, sniffing) induced by amphetamine is associated with a dopaminergic mechanism, and that the increase in locomotor activity involves a noradrenergic mechanism or both.

Almost all classes of psychotropic drugs interact in one way or another with catecholamine-containing neurons. Figures 6-6 and 6-7 outline the life cycle of the transmitters of dopaminergic and noradrenergic neurons in the central nervous system and indicate

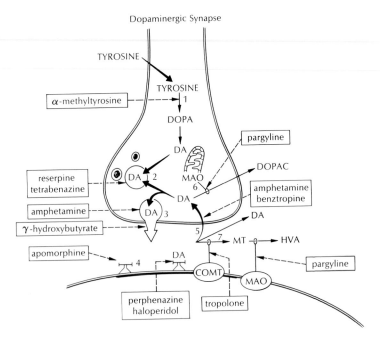

FIGURE 6-7. Schematic model of a central dopaminergic neuron indicating possible sites of drug action.

Step 1: Enzymatic synthesis: (a) Tyrosine hydroxylase reaction blocked by the competitive inhibitor, α-methyltyrosine and other tyrosine hydroxylase inhibitors (see Chapter 5).

Step 2: Storage. Reserpine and tetrabenazine interfere with the uptake-storage mechanism of the amine granules. The depletion of dopamine produced by reserpine is long-lasting and the storage granules appear to be irreversibly damaged. Tetrabenazine also interferes with the uptake-storage mechanism of the granules except that the effects of this drug do not appear to be irreversible.

Step 3: Release: γ-hydroxybutyrate effectively blocks the release of dopamine by blocking impulse flow in dopaminergic neurons. Amphetamine administered in high doses appears to cause release of dopamine but most of the releasing ability of amphetamine appears to be related to its ability to effectively block dopamine reuptake.

Step 4: Receptor interaction. Apomorphine appears to be an effective dopamine receptor stimulating drug, with both pre- and postsynaptic sites of action. Perphenazine and haloperidol are effective dopamine receptor blocking drugs.

Step 5: Reuptake: Dopamine appears to have its action terminated by being taken up into the presynaptic terminal. Amphetamine as well as the anticholinergic drug, benztropine, are potent inhibitors of this re-uptake mechanism.

Step 6: Monoamine Oxidase (MAO): Dopamine present in a free state within the presynaptic terminal can be degraded by the enzyme MAO which appears to be located in the outer membrane of the mitochondria. Dihydroxyphenylacetic acid (DOPAC) is a product of the action of MAO and aldehyde oxidase on dopamine. Pargyline is an effective inhibitor of MAO. Some MAO is also present outside the dopaminergic neuron.

Step 7: Catechol-O-methyltransferase (COMT): Dopamine can be inactivated by the enzyme COMT which is believed to be localized outside the presynaptic neuron. Tropolone is an inhibitor of COMT.

possible sites at which drugs may intervene in this cycle. These schematic models also provide examples of drugs or chemical agents which interfere at these various sites within the life cycle of the transmitter substances. These numerous sorts of interactions ultimately result in an increase, decrease, or no change in the functional activity of the catecholamine neuron in question.

Only recently it became possible to obtain a clear idea as to exactly how various pharmacological agents altered activity in defined catecholamine neuronal systems in the brain. In most cases the turnover of monoamines depends essentially upon impulse flow in the neuron. An increase in impulse flow usually causes an increase in turnover, and a decrease in impulse flow a reduction in turnover. As mentioned above, however, this is not always the case in the dopamine system if synthesis is used as an index of turnover. Measurement of turnover has been employed to gain some insight into the activity of various types of monoamine-containing neurons during different behavioral states or after administration of different psychotropic drugs. As might be predicted, psychotropic drugs can have a variety of effects, and these effects could alter the turnover of a given transmitter substance without necessarily altering impulse flow in the neuronal system under study. For example, a drug could have a direct effect on the synthesis, degradation, uptake, or release of a given transmitter which would in turn alter the turnover of the transmitter in question but would not necessarily lead to an increase or decrease in the activity of neuronal system which utilized that substance as a transmitter. So it becomes clear that an alteration in turnover of a transmitter is not necessarily a clear indication that there has been a change in impulse flow in a given neuronal pathway. Therefore, the most direct way to determine if a drug alters impulse flow in a chemically defined neuronal system is to measure the activity of that system while the animal is under the influence of the drug.

It now appears that there are also a number of ways in which drugs can alter impulse flow. For example, a drug can act directly on the nerve cell body; it can act on other neurons which then influence impulse flow in the neuron under study; or it can act at the postsynaptic receptor to cause stimulation or blockade which then results in some sort of feedback influence on the presynaptic neuron. This feedback information could either be neuronal or perhaps trans-synaptically mediated by release of some local chemical from the postsynaptic membrane. The recent combined histochemical-neurophysiological identification of dopaminergic and noradrenergic neurons has made possible the study of the effects of various drugs on the firing of these chemically defined neurons.

## Effect of Drugs on the Activity of Dopaminergic Neurons

More than a decade ago, entirely on the basis of indirect biochemical evidence, Swedish pharmacologists speculated that antipsychotic drugs, as a result of their ability to block dopaminergic

FIGURE 6-8. Effect of antipsychotic drugs on the firing rate of dopamine cells in the zona compacta of the rat.

(A) Effect of chlorpromazine on the activity of a dopaminergic cell in the zona compacta of a rat anesthetized with chloral hydrate. Chlorpromazine (CPZ) administered intravenously (iv) in divided doses of 0.5, 0.5, and 1.0 mg/kg caused a marked acceleration of the firing of this dopaminergic neuron.

(B) Effect of haloperidol on the activity of a dopaminergic cell in a non-anesthetized rat. An intravenous (iv) injection of haloperidol (HAL) 0.04 mg/kg increased basal activity about 100 per cent. (Courtesy of G. K. Aghajanian and B. S. Bunney.)

receptors, caused a feedback activation of dopaminergic neurons. Recently, direct extracellular recording experiments have validated these earlier speculations. Antipsychotic drugs of both the phenothiazine and butyrophenone classes cause a dramatic increase in the firing rate of dopamine neurons in rat brain (Fig. 6-8), an action presumably mediated by a neuronal feedback loop. Phenothiazines without antipsychotic potency are completely inactive in this regard. Of course, it is still a big jump to determine whether this interesting ability of antipsychotic drugs to block dopamine receptors is in any way related to their antipsychotic properties.

A naturally occurring metabolite of mammalian brain, $\gamma$-hydroxybutyrate, also has an interesting interaction with dopaminergic neurons. When $\gamma$-hydroxybutyrate is administered to rats in anesthetic doses, this compound causes a complete cessation of impulse flow in the nigro-neostriatal pathway (Fig. 6-9). This inhibition does not appear to be mediated *via* activation of a neuronal feedback loop. The activity of other monoamine-containing neurons such as the norepinephrine-containing neurons in the locus coeruleus or the 5-HT-containing neurons of the midbrain raphe, on the other hand, are relatively unaffected. Thus, this drug appears to be capable of producing a reversible lesion in the nigro-neostriatal and mesolimbic dopamine systems. The ability of this drug to block impulse flow in dopamine neurons most likely explains its unique biochemical properties as well as why it can effectively antagonize the ability of the antipsychotic drugs to increase the accumulation of dopamine metabolites in the striatum. Whether the drug will prove useful in the treatment of certain disease or drug-induced states such as Huntington's Chorea or tardive dyskinesias remains to be determined.

There is also compelling biochemical and behavioral evidence that amphetamine, L-dihydroxyphenylalanine, and apomorphine interact with dopamine neuronal systems in the CNS. Until recently, however, there has been no direct evidence that these drugs affect neuronal activity. Since all three drugs presumably lead either directly or indirectly to a stimulation of dopamine re-

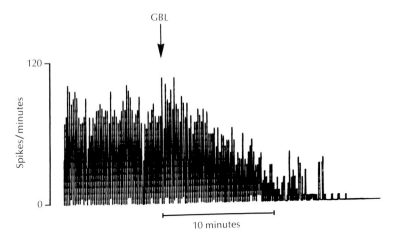

FIGURE 6-9. Typical response of a dopamine unit in the substantia nigra to γ-butyrolactone. This unit was situated in the zona compacta of the substantia nigra and had a spike frequency rate of about 1-2 spikes/sec. Within about 4 minutes following the injection of the lactone precursor of γ-hydroxybutyrate, γ-butyrolactone (GBL, 250 mg/kg, i.p.) this unit had significantly slowed. Fifteen minutes after γ-butyrolactone this unit had ceased firing almost entirely. (Courtesy of J. R. Walters.)

ceptors, it has been predicted that they might slow the activity of dopaminergic neurons via some sort of neuronal feedback loop. Recent extracellular unit recording experiments conducted on dopamine cells in the zona compacta and ventral tegmental area have borne out this speculation for all three drugs. In doses as low as 0.25 mg/kg, D-amphetamine inhibits firing of these dopamine neurons (Fig. 6-10). It appears to act indirectly through the release of newly synthesized dopamine since α-methyl-p-tyrosine can prevent or reverse the depression of dopamine cell firing. L-amphetamine will also inhibit the firing of dopaminergic neurons but is much less potent than D-amphetamine in producing this effect. L-dihydroxyphenylalanine also inhibits firing of these neurons and appears to exert its effects indirectly by being converted to dopamine. Pretreatment with a decarboxylase inhibitor will

FIGURE 6-10. Effect of D-amphetamine on the firing rate of a dopamine cell in the zona compacta. D-amphetamine (AMP) was administered intravenously at arrows in divided doses of 0.25 mg/kg. (Data from Bunney, Aghajanian, and Roth (1973).)

completely antagonize the inhibitory effect of dihydroxyphenyl-alanine on these cells. Apomorphine likewise appears to effectively inhibit the firing of dopamine cells, but this drug seems to act directly as its actions are not altered by inhibition of dopamine synthesis with α-methyl-p-tyrosine. It is also noteworthy that antipsychotic drugs have the ability to block and reverse the depressant effects of D-amphetamine, L-dihydroxyphenylalanine and apomorphine on the firing of dopamine cells. This observation suggests that all three drugs may exert their effects on firing rate through some sort of postsynaptic feedback pathway. Recent experiments indicate that apomorphine also has a direct effect on dopaminergic neurons of the nigro-neostriatal and mesolimbic systems.

### Effect of Drugs on the Activity of Noradrenergic Neurons

Amphetamine also alters the unit activity of noradrenergic neurons found in the locus coeruleus. It appears to inhibit the firing of these cells by activating a neuronal feedback loop; the effect is partially reversed by chlorpromazine. L-amphetamine is an equally potent inhibitor. Recent studies have also indicated that morphine administered to rats pretreated with flaxedil, a neuromuscular blocking agent, is effective in slowing the activity of noradrenergic units in the locus coeruleus which are firing at a faster rate during this rather stressful operative state.

Little is known about the effects of other psychotropic drugs on the firing of these cells. However, it is of interest that recent unit recording studies in unrestrained, unanesthetized cats have demonstrated that the norepinephrine-containing neurons in the locus coeruleus change their activity with sleep and wakefulness, becoming more active in attentive wakefulness and exhibiting bursting discharges during paradoxical sleep. This observation is consistent with the biochemical findings that norepinephrine turnover is increased during periods of increased paradoxical sleep.

CATECHOLAMINE THEORY OF AFFECTIVE DISORDERS

The catecholamines play a fairly well-established role in the periphery with regard to stress and emotional behavior. By contrast their suggested role in the central nervous system in affective disorders is still quite speculative although evidence for the involvement of these agents is becoming increasingly compelling.

A catecholamine hypothesis of affective disorder has arisen which states that, in general, behavioral depression may be related to a deficiency of catecholamine (usually norepinephrine) at functionally important central adrenergic receptors, while mania results from excess catecholamine. While substantial experimental work bears on this proposal it must be kept in mind that most of the experiments on which this hypothesis is based derive from "normal" animals. Secondly, from a nosological standpoint, depression itself is rather ill defined. In fact, Giarman has suggested that "nosologically it might be fair to compare the depressive syndrome with the anemias. Certainly, no self-respecting hematologist would subscribe to a unitary biochemical explanation for all of the anemias."

The original impetus for formulation of the catecholamine hypothesis was the finding that various monoamine oxidase inhibitors, notably iproniazid, acted clinically as mood elevators or anti-depressants. Shortly thereafter it was found that this class of compounds also produced marked increases in brain amine levels. By the same token, reserpine, a potent tranquilizer which causes depletion of brain amines, sometimes produces a serious depressed state (clinically indistinguishable from endogenous depression) and even suicidal attempts in man. Although both classes of drugs altered brain levels of catecholamines and serotonin quite equally, the fact that a precursor of catecholamine biosynthesis, notably DOPA, could reverse most of the reserpine-induced symptomology in animals has tended to bias many in favor of the catecholamine theory. In general, many pharmacological studies appear to implicate the catecholamines as the amines involved in affective disorders. However, it must be realized that a great deal more work has been done on norepinephrine than on other transmitter candidates. In fact, by no means does the available evidence obtained for the involvement of norepinephrine rule out the participation of dopamine, 5-hydroxytryptamine, or other putative transmitters in similar events.

The three general classes of drugs most commonly used to treat various depressive disorders are the monoamine oxidase inhibitors, the tricyclic antidepressants, and the psychomotor stimulants of which amphetamine was the prototype. All of these pharmacological agents appear to interact with catecholamines in a way which is consistent with the catecholamine hypothesis.

The amphetamines, even if one considers all the suggested modes of action—(a) partial agonist, mimicking action of norepinephrine at receptor, (b) inhibition of catecholamine re-uptake, (c) inhibition of monoamine oxidase, (d) displacement of norepinephrine, releasing it onto receptors—appear to exert an action compatible with the hypothesis above since the net result of all of these actions would be a temporary increase of norepinephrine at the receptor or a direct stimulatory action at the receptor. Upon administration of chronic or high doses of amphetamine it is possible to produce an eventual depletion of brain norepinephrine perhaps due to a displacement of norepinephrine in the neuron and/or an inhibition of synthesis. Also, as indicated earlier, amphetamine causes an inhibition of neuronal activity in catecholamine neurons. This chronic depletion of transmitter or a prolonged inactivity of catecholamine neurons may relate to the clinical observation of amphetamine tolerance or to the well-known poststimulation depression or fatigue observed after chronic administration of this class of drugs.

The tricyclic antidepressants may exert their action by inhibiting the catecholamine axonal membrane pump (see above). In support of this proposal the tricyclic antidepressants potentiate the peripheral autonomic effects of exogenous norepinephrine, the adrenergic responses elicited by both pre- and postganglionic sympathetic nerve stimulation, and the central effects of DOPA and amphetamine. In addition, their action is prevented by selective depletion of brain amines with $\alpha$-methyl-para-tyrosine as well as by administration of adrenergic blocking agents. While these findings are of course also consistent with the catecholamine hypothesis, the tricyclics do not affect this system exclusively. Thus, some of the tricyclic agents, notably imipramine, also potentiate peripheral and central effects of serotonin; they also have both central and peripheral anticholinergic actions.

The action of the monoamine oxidase inhibitors also supports the catecholamine hypothesis. All these agents inhibit an enzyme responsible for the metabolism of norepinephrine and various other amines (5-hydroxytryptamine, dopamine, tyramine, tryptamine). This inhibition results in a marked increase in the intraneuronal levels of norepinephrine. Presumably, according to the conceptual model of the adrenergic neuron presented above, this interneuronal norepinephrine might eventually diffuse out of the neuron and reach receptor cells, thus overcoming the presumed deficiency. A similar mechanism may also explain the antagonism of reserpine-induced sedation with monoamine oxidase inhibitors, since there will be a replenishment of the norepinephrine deficiency initially caused by reserpine.

Lithium, one of the main agents used in the treatment of mania has also been studied with regard to its action on the life cycle of the catecholamines. Interestingly, pretreatment with lithium blocks the stimulus-induced release of norepinephrine from rat brain slices. Other investigators have suggested that lithium may facilitate re-uptake of norepinephrine. If the inhibition of release observed in stimulated brain slices is due to a facilitated recapture mechanism, then the mechanism of action of lithium would be the exact opposite of that of the antidepressant drugs, as would be expected according to the catecholamine hypothesis.

SELECTED REFERENCES

Bunney, B. S., G. K. Aghajanian, and R. H. Roth (1973). L-DOPA, amphetamine and apomorphine: comparison of effects on the firing rate of rat dopaminergic neurons. *Nature 245*, 123.

Bunney, B. S., J. R. Walters, R. H. Roth, and G. K. Aghajanian (1973). Dopaminergic neurons: effect of antipsychotic drugs and amphetamine on single cell activity. *J. Pharmacol. Exp. Ther. 185*, 560.

Chu, N., and F. E. Bloom (1973). Norepinephrine-containing neurons: changes in spontaneous discharge patterns during sleeping and waking. *Science 179*, 908.

Dahlström, A., and K. Fuxe (1965). Evidence for the existence of monoamine-containing neurons in the central nervous system. I. Demonstration of monoamines in the cell bodies on brain stem neurons. *Acta Physiol. Scand. 62*, suppl. 232, 1.

Giarman, N. J. (1968). Modes and sites of action of psychic energizers. In *Mind as a Tissue*. Hoeber, New York, p. 123.

Hornykiewicz, O. (1966). Dopamine (3-hydroxytyramine) and brain function. *Pharmacol. Rev. 18*, 925.

Kety, S. S. (1967). Current biochemical approaches to schizophrenia. *New Eng. J. Med. 276*, 325.

Roth, R. H. (1973). Striatal dopamine and γ-hydroxybutyrate. In *The International Encyclopedia of Pharmacology and Therapeutics*, Vol. 25, *The Pharmacology of the Extrapyramidal System*. Pergamon Press, New York.

Roth, R. H., J. R. Walters, and G. K. Aghajanian (1973). Effect of impulse flow on the release and synthesis of dopamine in the rat striatum. In *Frontiers in Catecholamine Research*, E. Usdin and S. Snyder (eds.), Pergamon Press, New York, in press.

Schildkraut, J. J. (1973). Neuropharmacology of the affective disorders. *Ann. Rev. Pharmacol. 13*, 427.

Snyder, S. H. (1972). Catecholamines in the brain as mediators of amphetamine psychosis. *Arch. Gen. Psychiat. 27*, 169.

Snyder, S. H., K. M. Taylor, J. T. Coyle, and J. L. Meyerhoff (1970). The role of brain dopamine in behavioral regulation and the actions of psychotropic drugs. *Amer. J. Psychiat.* *127*, 199.

Ungerstedt, U. (1971). Stereotaxic mapping of the monoamine pathways in the rat brain. *Acta Physiol. Scand.*, suppl. 367, 1.

# 7 | Serotonin (5-hydroxytryptamine)

*Historical Introduction*

Of all the neurotransmitter substances we shall discuss, serotonin is the one whose history is most intimately involved with neuropsychopharmacology. Since the middle of the nineteenth century, scientists have been aware of a substance found in the serum of clotted blood which had the ability to cause powerful constriction of smooth muscle organs. Not until the mid-twentieth century did scientists at the Cleveland Clinic succeed in isolating this substance as a possible cause of high blood pressure. At the same time, investigators in Italy were busily trying to characterize the substance found in high concentrations in enterochromaffin cells of the intestinal mucosa. This material also had the ability to cause constriction of smooth muscular elements, particularly those of the gut. The material isolated from the bloodstream was given the name "serotonin" while that from the intestinal tract was called "enteramine." Subsequently, both materials were crystallized and shown to be identical with 5-hydroxytryptamine (5-HT) which could then be prepared synthetically, and shown to possess all the biological features of the natural substance. The indole nature of this molecule bore many resemblances to the psychedelic drug LSD, with which it could be shown to interact on smooth muscle preparations *in vitro*.

When 5-HT was first found within the mammalian central nervous system, the theory arose that various forms of mental illness could be due to biochemical abnormalities in its synthesis. This line of thought was even further extended when the tranquilizing substance, reserpine, was observed to deplete brain 5-HT; throughout the duration of the depletion, profound behavioral depression was observed. As we shall see, many of these ideas and theories are still maintained although we have much more ample evidence now on which to evaluate them.

## Occurrence

Indolealkyl amines (Fig. 7-1), including serotonin, occur widely in nature. For example, many types of fruits such as pineapples and bananas contain extremely large amounts of 5-HT. In mammals, the highest concentration of this amine occurs in the pineal gland and in the enterochromaffin cells of the intestinal tract. In man, it is estimated that about 90 per cent of the body's serotonin occurs in the gastrointestinal tract, another 8 to 10 per cent in platelets, and only 1 to 2 per cent within the central nervous sys-

FIGURE. 7-1. Structural relationships of the various indolealkyl amines.

| Compound | Substitutions |
|---|---|
| Tryptamine | $R_1$ and $R_2$ = H |
| Serotonin | Tryptamine with 5 Hydroxy |
| Melatonin | 5 methoxy, N—acetyl |
| DMT* | $R_1$ and $R_2$ = methyl |
| DET* | $R_1$ and $R_2$ = ethyl |
| Bufotenine* | 5 hydroxy, DMT |
| Szara psychotrope* | 6 hydroxy, DET |
| Psilocin* | 4 hydroxy, DMT |
| Harmaline* | 6 methoxy; $R_1$ forms isopropyl link to $C_2$. |
| 5-MT | 5-methoxytryptamine |
| 5,6 DHT | 5,6 dihydroxytryptamine |
| 5,7 DHT | 5,7 dihydroxytryptamine |

* = psychotropic or behavioral effects.

tem. In many of the laboratory animals, such as rats and mice, an additional tissue source of serotonin comes from the mast cell.

## BIOSYNTHESIS OF SEROTONIN

While serotonin does occur naturally in brain, it does not enter the brain readily from the blood stream because of its solubility characteristics. Therefore, we must now inquire into the methods by which the brain is able to synthesize its own serotonin.

The first step appears to be the uptake of the amino acid tryptophan, which is the primary substrate for the synthesis. Plasma tryptophan arises primarily from the diet, and elimination of dietary tryptophan can profoundly lower the levels of brain serotonin. In addition, an active uptake process is known to facilitate the entry of tryptophan into cells, and this entry site can be competed for by certain other amino acids, such as phenylalanine. Because plasma tryptophan has a daily rhythmic variation in its concentration, it seems likely that this concentration variation could profoundly influence the rate and synthesis of brain serotonin.

The next step in the pathway to synthesize serotonin is to hydroxylate the molecule at the 5 position (Fig. 7-2) to form 5-hydroxytryptophan (5-HTP). The enzyme responsible for this reaction, tryptophan hydroxylase, occurs in low concentrations in most tissues, including the brain, and it was very difficult to isolate for study. After purifying the enzyme from mast cell tumors and determining the characteristic cofactors, however, it became possible to characterize this enzyme in the brain. (Students should investigate the ingenious methods used for the initial assays of this extremely minute enzyme activity.) The enzyme, as isolated from the brain, appears to have an absolute requirement for molecular oxygen, reduced pteridine cofactor, and to require a sulfhydryl stabilizing substance, such as mercaptoethanol, for preservation of activity *in vitro*. With this fortified system of assay there is sufficient activity in the brain to synthesize one $\mu$g of 5-HTP per gram of brain stem in an hour. The pH maximum is approximately 7.2 and the $K_m$ for tryptophan is $3 \times 10^{-4}$M. Additional

FIGURE 7-2. The metabolic pathways available for the synthesis and metabolism of serotonin.

research into the nature of the endogenous cofactor, tetrahydro-biopterin, yielded a $K_m$ for tryptophan of $5 \times 10^{-5}M$, which is still above normal tryptophan concentrations. As it has been characterized thus far, tryptophan hydroxylase appears to be a soluble cytoplasmic enzyme; however, it must be remembered that the procedures used to extract it from the tissues may greatly alter the natural particle-binding capacity. Investigators examining the relative distribution of particulate and soluble tryptophan hydroxylase have reported that the particulate enzyme may be associated with 5-HT-containing synapses, while the soluble form is more likely to be associated with the perikaryal cytoplasm. The particulate form of the enzyme shows the lower $K_m$ and bears an absolute requirement for tetrahydrobiopterin. This step in the synthesis can be specifically blocked by *p*-chlorophenylalanine, which competes directly with the tryptophan and also binds irreversibly to the enzyme. Therefore, recovery from tryptophan hydroxylase inhibition with *p*-chlorophenylalanine appears to require the synthesis of new enzyme molecules. In the rat, a single intraperitoneal injection of 300 mg/kg of this inhibitor lowers the brain serotonin content to less than 20 per cent within three days, and complete recovery does not occur for almost two weeks.

## Decarboxylation

Following its synthesis, 5-HTP is almost immediately decarboxylated to yield serotonin. The enzyme responsible for this was presumed to be identical with the enzyme that decarboxylates dihydroxyphenylalanine (DOPA). This information was gained mainly by the study of decarboxylase activities which were partially purified from liver or kidney and of the regional distribution of enzyme activity. More recent studies permit a reconsideration of this viewpoint that catecholamine-synthesizing neurons and serotonin-synthesizing neurons possess exactly the same protein to perform decarboxylations. When the decarboxylation step is examined in brain homogenates, the activity for DOPA differs widely from 5-HTP with respect to pH, temperature, and substrate optima; and within the homogenate subfractions, the two activities become enriched in different subfractions—that of the 5-HTP decarboxylase being mainly associated with the synaptosomal and DOPA decarboxylase with the soluble fraction. Finally, the case for two separate enzymes is supported by the observation that treatment of animals with intracisternal 6-hydroxydopamine (see Chapters 5 and 6) reduces DOPA decarboxylase activity but not decarboxylase 5-HTP activity. On the other hand, immune sera raised against the decarboxylase purified from kidney cross-react with both decarboxylases from brain, perhaps indicating that many common antigenic determinants are shared. Since this decarboxylation reaction occurs so rapidly, and since its $K_m$ ($5 \times 10^{-6}M$) requires less substrate than the preceding steps, tryptophan hydroxylase would appear to be the rate-limiting step in the synthesis of serotonin, providing the added tryptophan is available in the controlled state. Because of this kinetic relationship, drug-induced inhibition of serotonin by interference with the decarboxylation step has never proven particularly effective.

*Catabolism*

For the most part, following its synthesis, the only effective route of continued metabolism for serotonin is to be deaminated by the enzyme monoamine oxidase. This enzyme is identical in all known characteristics with that which catabolizes the catecholamines. The product of this reaction, 5-hydroxyindoleacetaldehyde can be further oxidized to 5-hydroxyindoleacetic acid (5-HIAA) or reduced to 5-hydroxytryptophol depending on the $NAD^+/NADH$ ratio in the tissue. Recently enzymes have been described in liver and brain by which 5-HT could be catabolized without deamination through formation of a 5-sulfate ester. This could then be transported out of brain, possibly by the acid excretion system handling 5-HIAA. Most recently, data have been obtained which indicate that there may in fact be more than one monoamine oxidase isozyme in brain, and that one isozyme shows preferential substrate affinity for 5-HT.

Brain contains an enzyme which will catalyze the N-methylation of 5-HT using S-adenosylmethionine as the methyl donor. It has been observed that brain also contains an N-methylating enzyme which utilizes 5-methyl tetrahydrofolate as the methyl donor. This enzyme appears to be rather non-specific in that in addition to N-methylating indoleamines it will also N-methylate phenylethylamine derivatives such as dopamine to form epinine (see Chapter 5).

*Control of Serotonin Synthesis and Catabolism*

Although there is a relatively brief sequence of synthetic and degradative steps involved in serotonin turnover, there is still much to be learned regarding the physiological mechanisms for controlling this pathway. At first glance, it seems clear that tryptophan hydroxylase is the rate-limiting enzyme in the synthesis of serotonin, since when this enzyme is inhibited by 80 per cent, the serotonin content of the brain rapidly decreases. On the other hand, when the 5-HTP decarboxylase is inhibited by equal or greater amounts, there is no effect upon the level of brain 5-HT. These data could only be explained if the important rate-limiting step were the initial hydroxylation. Since this step also depends upon molecular oxygen, the rate of 5-HT formation could also be influenced by the tissue level of oxygen. In fact, it can be shown that rats permitted to breathe 100 per cent oxygen greatly increase their synthesis of 5-HT. It is also of interest that 5-hydroxytryptophan does not inhibit the activity of tryptophan hydroxylase.

If the situation for serotonin were similar to that previously described for the catecholamines, we might also expect that the concentration of 5-HT itself could influence the levels of activity at the hydroxylation step. However, when the catabolism of 5-HT is blocked by monoamine oxidase inhibitors, the brain 5-HT concentration accumulates linearly to levels three times greater than controls, thus suggesting that end-product inhibition by serotonin is, at best, trivial. Similarly, if the efflux of 5-HIAA from the brain is blocked by the drug probenecid (which appears to block all forms of acidic transport) the 5-HIAA levels also continue to rise linearly for prolonged periods of time, again suggesting that the initial synthesis step is not affected by the levels of any of the subsequent metabolites. Two possibilities therefore remain open: the initial synthesis rate may be limited only by the access of required cofactors or substrate, such as oxygen, pteridine, and tryptophan from the bloodstream, or by other more subtle control features, more closely related to brain activity. Before we consider the experiments which suggest that neuronal activity may influence the synthesis and metabolism of brain serotonin, we should be aware that 5-HT may not be the only active indoleamine found in the brain. On the basis of fluorescence histochemistry, a second family of indoleamine-containing neurons has been described in the raphe nuclei, but their axonal projections have not been presented in detail. Aside from a different fluorescent spectrum and greater resistance to decomposition in ultraviolet light, the second indoleamine is not depleted by $p$-chlorphenylalanine. This may either mean that 5-hydroxylation is unnecessary or that the somatic enzyme recovers very rapidly from the drug.

## PINEAL

The pineal organ is a tiny gland (1 mg or less in the rodent) contained within connective tissue extensions of the dorsal surface of the thalamus. While physically connected to the brain, the pineal is cytologically isolated for all intents, since it is on the "peripheral" side of the blood permeability barriers (see Chapter 2) and since its exclusive innervation arises from the superior cervical sympathetic ganglion. The pineal is of interest for two reasons. First, it contains all the enzymes required for the synthesis of serotonin, and two enzymes for subsequent use of the serotonin that are found in no other organs. In fact, the pineal contains more than fifty times as much 5-HT per gram as the whole brain. Second, the metabolic activity of the pineal 5-HT enzymes can be controlled by numerous external factors, including the neural activity of the sympathetic nervous system operating through release of norepinephrine. As such, the pineal appears to offer us a potential model for the study of brain 5-HT.

Actually, the 5-HT content of the pineal was discovered after the isolation of a pineal factor, melatonin, known to induce pigment lightening effects on skin cells. When melatonin was crystallized and its chemical structure determined as 5-methoxy-N-acetyltryptamine, an indolealkylamine, a reasonable extension was to analyze the pineal for 5-HT itself. The production of melatonin from 5-HT requires two additional enzymatic steps. The first is the N-acetylation reaction to form N-acetylserotonin. This intermediate is the preferred substrate for the final step, the 5-hydroxy indole-O-methyltransferase reaction, requiring S-adenosyl methionine as the methyl donor.

The melatonin content, and its influence in suppressing the female gonads, was subsequently found to be enhanced by environmental light and suppressed by darkness. In fact, the established cyclic daily rhythm of both 5-HT and melatonin in the pineal appear to be directly related to environmental lighting patterns. Furthermore, this effect requires the presence of an intact sympathetic innervation, since chronically denervated pineal behaves biochemically like the pineal of a blinded animal. However, the controlling step by which the nerve impulses influence melatonin synthesis (and presumably the secretion from the pineal into the bloodstream) appears to be at the O-methylation step rather than earlier in the synthesis of 5-HT. Thus, the proposed model's applicability to brain 5-HT loses its lustre since this regulatory step does not seem to be of functional importance in the central nervous system. Furthermore, the "adrenergic" sympathetic nerves are now known to be able to take up 5-HT as well as they can take up and bind norepinephrine. Whether this is a functional mistake (to be able to secrete an endogenous false transmitter) or is simply a case of mistaken biologic identity, remains to be shown. It seems likely, however, that it is the neuronal norepinephrine whose release is required to pass on the intended communications from the sympathetic nervous system. The norepinephrine may cause its effects in the postjunctional cells by stimulating the synthesis of $3', 5'$ adenosine monophosphate (cyclic AMP) which in turn provides a controlling message to the sites synthesizing melatonin.

## Localizing Brain Serotonin to Nerve Cells

While some of these pineal curiosities may prove to be useful for the study of brain 5-HT, they are no substitute for data derived directly from brain. If we attempt to relate changes in brain 5-HT and 5-HT metabolites to changes in brain activity with drug treatments or with different behavioral states, we must ascertain that brain serotonin is contained within nerve fibers. Although the brain content of serotonin was discovered in 1953, it was nearly ten years before scientists developed techniques which permitted us to know with certainty that the serotonin of the brain was contained in neurons. The first support for this view arose from studies on brain homogenates (see Chapter 3) in which it could be shown that the synaptosome fraction was rich in serotonin and 5-HTP-decarboxylase.

While this finding suggested only a general relationship to nerve terminals, two other techniques quickly appeared which related 5-HT to specific nerve tracts much more succinctly. A classical neuroanatomical approach has been to produce lesions and to follow the distribution of the degenerating axons. By combining this approach with biochemical measurements, Heller and Moore placed lesions in the medial forebrain bundle of the hypothalamus and observed that the forebrain concentration of serotonin dropped dramatically over the next 5 to 12 days (see Chapter 3). These data strongly suggested that a nerve pathway containing serotonin passed through the lateral hypothalamus; when the pathway was interrupted, degeneration of the axons resulted in loss of serotonin. At almost the same point in time, the Swedish histochemical group led by Hillarp and Falck, perfected the technique for using fluorescence histochemistry to reveal the distribution of monoamine-containing nerve fibers and cell bodies in the central nervous system. By this technique, almost all the serotonin-containing cell bodies were found to be restricted to a narrow group of neurons, known as the raphe nuclei, lying in the mid-portion of the lower pons and upper brain stem (Fig. 7-3). Their fibers to the forebrain would follow the path predictable by the lesioning method of Heller and Moore. In many other laboratories, using different species of mammals, other investigators have established that by placing lesions at selected points along this postulated pathway from brain stem to forebrain or spinal cord, pre-

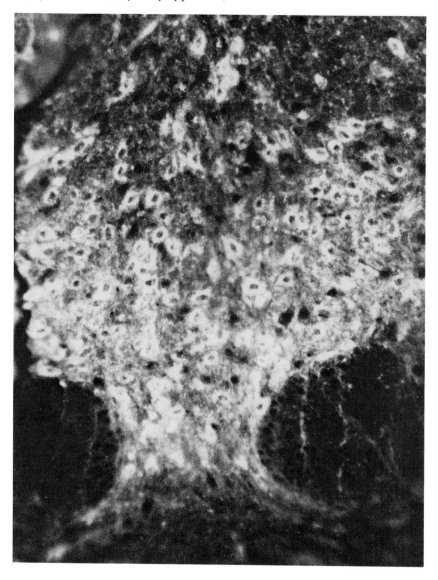

FIGURE 7-3. Fluorescence micrograph of raphe cell bodies in the midbrain of the rat. This rat was pretreated with L-tryptophan (100 mg/kg) one hour prior to sacrifice. (Courtesy of G. K. Aghajanian.)

FIGURE 7-4. Dark field fluorescence micrograph of serotonin-containing nerve terminals within the ventral lateral geniculate nucleus of the rat after inhibition of monoamine oxidase and loading with parenteral tryptophan. These nerve terminals measure approximately 1-3$\mu$, although many appear even finer. (Courtesy of G. K. Aghajanian.)

dictable drops of serotonin occur—provided the lesions are extensive enough to remove most of the raphe nuclei. However, very small lesions of individual portions of the raphe nuclei do not result in complete elimination of serotonin from any part of the rat's brain; this indicates that the raphe nuclei are likely to have extremely diffuse and presumably overlapping fields of innervation. However, complete destruction of the raphe system with electrolytic lesions does result in a more or less proportional decrement in the content of 5-HT and of synthetic enzymes throughout the forebrain, confirming the axonal projection systems described by the microscopic methods (Fig. 7-4).

It would seem pertinent to attempt to localize the serotonin-containing nerves with electron microscopy. The numerous attempts to do so have concentrated mainly upon the cellular distribution and morphological characteristics of the nerve terminals arising from the raphe neurons. These nerve terminals can be identified in two ways. The easier way is to examine areas rich in the fluorescence labeling for serotonin nerve terminals; an alternative method is to attempt to label the endogenous stores of serotonin by intraventricular injection of radioactive serotonin. The latter technique is based on the assumption that serotonin-containing neurons exhibit a specific uptake mechanism for their amine similar to that found in the catecholamine-containing neuron (see Chapter 5). After intraventricular injection of radioactive serotonin, the majority of the nerve terminals that are labeled exhibit large granular vesicles and numerous small electronlucent vesicles. These nerve terminals are in a regional distribution which generally agrees with that described by fluorescence histochemistry. When brain slices from 5-HT-rich regions are incubated *in vitro* with a false marker, such as $\alpha$-methyl norepinephrine, and then fixed with cold $KMnO_4$, nerve terminals in those portions of the brain which normally contain serotonin can be shown to exhibit small electron-dense synaptic vesicles just as those described for the norepinephrine-containing neurons. Furthermore, when lesions are made in the raphe nuclei, degenerative changes in these types of nerve endings can be found in the serotonin-rich neuropil of the suprachiasmatic nucleus. However, each of these methods is based on an indirect mechanism for revealing serotonin and no discrete specific histochemical technique with practical application to the central nervous system has yet been worked out.

CELLULAR EFFECTS OF 5-HT

From the biochemical and morphological data above we can be relatively certain that the 5-HT of the brain occurs not only within the nerve cells but within specific tracts or projections of nerve cells. We must now inquire into the effects of serotonin when applied at the cellular level (see Chapter 2). In those brain areas in which microelectrophoretically administered 5-HT has been tested on cells which exhibit spontaneous electrical activity, the majority of nerve fibers are found to respond by decreasing their discharge rate. The effects observed typically last much longer than the duration of the microelectrophoretic current. However, in certain portions of the brain, particularly the limbic cortex, 5-HT can also be shown to cause pronounced activation of discharge rate. Since activation with 5-HT occurs much less commonly than depression with 5-HT, data are needed to verify that the activation response does not arise secondarily from inhibition of adjacent inhibitory interneurons.

However, in the simpler nervous system of molluscs, the application of serotonin can be shown to cause pronounced depolarization of cells being recorded with intracellular electrodes and there can be little question of the site of action. Rather convincing data on the vagal inhibitory reflex indicate that serotonin-containing interneurons may play an integral role in control of gastric contractions. If such is the case, then all other peripheral autonomic ganglia, in which serotonin content has been attributed to mast cells, will have to be reinvestigated.

In the mammalian central nervous system, however, we as yet have no specific synaptic connection which we can analyze for the effects of neurally released serotonin as compared with the effects of serotonin administered by micropipettes. Because of this acute lack of information, it is impossible to evaluate objectively the multiple reports in the literature concerning the specificity of alleged central serotonin blocking agents which affect neuronal and behavioral activity. Furthermore, practically no data exist on which we could predict whether or not such presumptive serotonin-mediated synapses are more likely to be excitatory or inhibitory or whether they are to control primary neurons or interneurons. This distinct lack of basic information should be borne in mind as we now review the cellular pharmacology and multicellular effects attributable to the serotonin system of the brain.

*Cellular Pharmacology of Brain Serotonin*

Let us first consider whether or not a dynamic re-uptake and turnover of serotonin occurs in a fashion similar to that described above for the catecholamines. If we attempt to use the same techniques, namely, to place a small amount of radioactive serotonin, into the ventricle to label the endogeneous stores of serotonin, and follow the decline in specific radioactivity of serotonin in the brain, we find that the serotonin half-life is very long, on the order of 4 to 5 hrs after the initial acute drop is over. When this ventricular labeling technique is verified by fluorescence histochemistry or light-microscopic or electron-microscopic autoradiography, the majority of the uptake is seen to be into those nerves that normally contain serotonin, but the labeling is mainly over terminals and axons with very little labeling within the cell body area. Therefore, we know, initially, that the labeling of the serotonin pool by these injection techniques is not complete and that the decline in radioactivity does not reflect total brain 5-HT. Furthermore, if we use any of the other methods for estimating turnover, such as inhibiting monoamine oxidase and following the rate of rise of serotonin, or inhibiting the efflux of 5-HIAA from the brain, we find that the biochemical estimate of this turnover is considerably faster than that determined by the labeling with radioactive 5-HT.

There would seem to be at least two explanations for this kinetic discrepancy. One would be that the uptake for serotonin is, in some respect, less selective or specific than that for the catecholamines. However, the uptake system appears to be similar in that it is energy dependent, that is, it is much more active at 37°C than at 0°, it requires both glucose and oxygen, and can be inhibited by ouabain, dinitrophenol, or iodoacetate. Furthermore, the uptake system for 5-HT can be partially inhibited by the same types of drugs which inhibit the uptake of catecholamine into catecholamine-containing nerve endings, such as desmethylimipramine, chlorpromazine, or cocaine, when evaluated on brain slices. When the nerve slices are stimulated, the serotonin previously taken up can be released into the media, suggesting—again —that the binding and release are by functional nerve fibers of a specific selective class.

On the other hand, when the turnover rates of brain serotonin (that is, complete whole brain serotonin) are estimated by using precursor labeling (i.e. tryptophan) and determining specific activity changes with time, results are mainly compatible with the fast rather than the slow turnover time of serotonin. The logical tentative conclusion to be reached then is that the pool of neuronal serotonin which the ventricular injection most readily labels consists mainly of the excess or storage form of serotonin, whereas total endogenous serotonin, in terms of synthesis and utilization, is turned over much more rapidly. These findings would suggest that a great deal of serotonin resides in the storage form, patiently awaiting the call to action. For many years, virtually the only specific pharmacologic tool available for studying the role of 5-HT in the brain was $p$-chlorophenylalanine. In the pursuit of additional specific pharmacological tools, however, it was discovered that 5,6 dihydroxytryptamine can produce a selective long term destruction of 5-HT axons and terminals in the brain, similar to the effects of 6-OHDA on the catecholamines. 5,6-DHT is more toxic and produces less extensive destruction, and has so far found its greatest utility after local microinjections and for fluorescence and electron microscopy. Recently, there has been a reawakening of interest in $p$-chloroamphetamine, which for reasons that remain unclear produces long lasting 5-HT depletion.

## The Reserpine Story

One of the first drugs found empirically to be effective as a central tranquilizing agent, reserpine, was employed mainly for its action against hypertension. In the early 1950's when both brain serotonin and the central effects of reserpine were first described, there was great excitement when it was shown that the dramatic effects of reserpine upon the brain were to deplete the serotonin content. However, it shortly became clear that the norepinephrine

and dopamine content of the brain could also be depleted by reserpine and that the depletion lasted longer than the sedative action. The brain levels would remain down for weeks while the
acute behavioral effect was over within 48 to 72 hours. Hence, it
became difficult to determine whether it was the loss of brain
catecholamine or serotonin which accounted for the behavioral
depression after reserpine. Perhaps in passing we should note the
possibility that the behavioral effect and the biochemical effect
might both be epi-phenomena of some more basic brain action.

Experiments were then performed which were mainly pseudo-
behavioral in context, in which the reserpine-induced depression
was combated by injecting heroic amounts of precursor amino
acids, namely, 5-HTP or DOPA. When this is done, 5-HTP increased the sedation, but in even larger doses caused excitation.
However, the recovery from reserpine-induced sedation was not
typically related to the return of the brain serotonin level that resulted from the 5-HTP administration. On the other hand, when
DOPA was injected (although the doses required are really quite
large with respect to the amount of amine in the brain) the reserpine symptoms could be reversed. Furthermore, it was found that
by treating with small doses of reserpine for long periods of time,
one could deplete practically all of the brain catecholamines without causing behavioral symptoms, but when a subsequent large
dose of reserpine was given and the norepinephrine content
dropped an additional 10 per cent, the behavioral depression
symptoms appeared.

All these experiments then were interpreted as favoring the
view that depression after reserpine was mainly due to loss of
brain catecholamines. However, we should note that the enzyme
which catabolizes both these precursor amino acids is the same,
and until it can be shown that the nerve terminals have the specific uptake mechanisms for the appropriate amino acid precursor
but not the related amino acid, these findings alone do not necessarily give the correct answer to the reserpine problem.

More extensive experiments into the nature of this problem
were possible when the drugs which specifically block the syn-

thesis of catecholamines or serotonin were discovered. After depleting brain serotonin content with parachlorophenylalanine, which effectively removed 90 per cent of brain serotonin, investigators observed that no behavioral symptoms reminiscent of the reserpine syndrome appeared. Moreover, when $p$-chlorophenylalanine-treated rats, which were already devoid of measurable serotonin, were treated with reserpine, typical reserpine-induced sedation arose. These results again favor the view that loss of catecholamines could be responsible for the reserpine-induced syndrome. Furthermore, when $\alpha$-methyl-$p$-tyrosine is given and synthesis of norepinephrine is blocked for prolonged periods of time, the animals are behaviorally sedated and their condition resembles the depression seen after reserpine. Therefore, after fifteen years of intensive work upon the possible cellular explanation for the behavioral action of reserpine, we are able to explain this action partially. The students will find it profitable to review in detail the original papers describing the results just summarized, and the other theories currently in vogue.

*Hallucinogenic Drugs*

One of the more alluring aspects of the study of brain serotonin is the possibility that it is this serotinergic system of neurons through which the hallucinogenic drugs cause their effects. In the early 1950's the concept arose that LSD might produce its behavioral effects in the brain by interfering with the action of serotonin there as it did in smooth muscle preparations, such as the rat uterus. However, this theory of LSD action was not supported by the finding that another serotonin blocking agent, 2-bromo LSD, produced minimal behavioral effects in the central nervous system. And, in fact, it was subsequently shown that very low concentrations of LSD itself—rather than blocking the serotonin action—could potentiate it. However, none of these data could be considered particularly pertinent since all the research was done on the peripheral nervous system and all the philosophy was applied to the central nervous system.

Shortly thereafter Freedman and Giarman initiated a profitable series of experiments investigating the basic biochemical changes in the rodent brain following injection of LSD. Although their initial studies required them to use bioassay for changes in serotonin, they were able to detect a small (on the order of 100 ng/g, or less) increase in the serotonin concentration of the rat brain shortly after the injection of very small doses of LSD. Subsequent studies have shown that a decrease in 5-HIAA accompanies the small rise in 5-HT. Although the biochemical effects are similar to those that would be seen from small doses of monoamine oxidase inhibitors, no direct monoamine oxidase inhibitory effect of LSD has been described. This effect was generally interpreted as indicating a temporary decrease in the rate at which serotonin was being broken down, and it could also be seen with higher doses of less effective psychoactive drugs. In related studies by Costa and his coworkers, who estimated the biochemical turnover of brain serotonin, prolonged infusion of somewhat larger doses of LSD clearly promoted a decrease in the turnover rate of brain serotonin.

The next advance in the explanation of the LSD response was made when Aghajanian and Sheard reported that electrical stimulation of the raphe nuclei would selectively increase the metabolism of 5-HT to 5-HIAA. This finding suggested that the electrical activity of the 5-HT cells could be directly reflected in the metabolic turnover of the amine. Subsequently, the same authors recorded single raphe neurons during parenteral administration of LSD and observed that they slowed down with a time course similar to the effect of LSD. Thus, following LSD administration both decreased electrical activity of these cells and decreased transmitter turnover occur. Two explanations for these events have been provided; one is that the LSD occupies serotonin receptor sites and thus activates some undefined feedback mechanism whereby the activity of the serotonin neurons is inhibited. On the other hand, the effects of LSD could be mediated by a direct inhibition of the serotonin-containing cells, either by a metabolic action or by blocking those neurotransmitters that normally activate these cells. Recently the latter point has been partially supported by data indicating that activation of raphe cells by either norepinephrine or 5-HT applied electrophoretically can be blocked by LSD.

Even though we can offer almost complete explanations for the biochemical parameters on 5-HT accompanying the effects of LSD, can we explain the behavioral responses to LSD in terms of these mechanisms? That is to say, if the effects of LSD as reflected in abnormalities of 5-HT metabolism were due primarily or exclusively to interactions with the raphe nuclei, then we should be able to reproduce the behavioral effects by other similar mechanisms. In light of the foregoing experiments, one might expect that removal of the raphe system would closely mimic the effects of LSD if the latter serves only to block 5-HT synapses. However, the physiological manipulation which most closely reproduces certain of the behavioral features of the LSD response, namely, failure to habituate to sensory stimuli, is best reproduced by electrical stimulation of the raphe nuclei. These data would suggest that at least a portion of the behavioral symptomatology requires the activation of the receptors opposite serotonin-containing nerve endings. There are other psychoactive drugs whose basic chemical structure is similar to that of serotonin (see Table 7-1). However, the majority of these compounds are much less active on a weight basis as compared with LSD, and explanation for their cellular mechanism of action will be even more difficult.

*Actions of Other Psychotropic Drugs*

Subsequent studies by Aghajanian and his colleagues have indicated that other drugs which can alter 5-HT metabolism can also disturb the discharge pattern of the raphe neurons. Thus, monamine oxidase inhibitors and tryptophan, which would be expected to elevate brain 5-HT levels, also slow raphe discharge; while clinically effective tricyclic drugs (anti-depressants such as imipramine, chlorimipramine, and amitryptyline) also slow the raphe neurons and could elevate brain 5-HT levels locally by inhibition of 5-HT re-uptake. At the present time it remains unclear whether these metabolic changes in 5-HT after psychoactive drugs are administered reflect changes in the cells which receive 5-HT synapses or in the raphe neurons themselves. A larger question is whether these circuits mediate the therapeutic responses of the drugs or are the primary pathologic site of the diseases the drugs treat. One etiologic view of schizophrenia, for example, might be based on the production of an abnormal indole, such as the hallucinogenic dimethyltryptamine, a compound that can be formed in human plasma from tryptamine. Recent evidence indicates that schizophrenic patients have abnormally low monoamine oxidase activity in their platelets, which could permit the formation of abnormal amounts of plasma tryptamine and consequently abnormal amounts of dimethyltryptamine as well. Figure 7-5

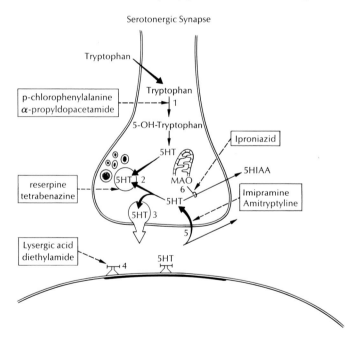

FIGURE 7-5. Schematic model of a central serotonergic neuron indicating possible sites of drug action.
Site 1: Enzymatic synthesis: Tryptophan is taken up into the sero-

tonin-containing neuron and converted to 5-OH-tryptophan by the enzyme tryptophan hydroxylase. This enzyme can be effectively inhibited by $p$-chlorophenylalanine and α-propyldopacetamide. The next synthetic step involves the decarboxylation of 5-OH-tryptophan to form serotonin (5-HT).

Site 2: Storage: Reserpine and tetrabenazine interfere with the uptake-storage mechanism of the amine granules causing a marked depletion of serotonin.

Site 3: Release: At present there is no drug available which selectively blocks the release of serotonin. However, lysergic acid diethylamide, due to its ability to block or inhibit the firing of serotonin neurons, causes a reduction in the release of serotonin from the nerve terminals.

Site 4: Receptor interaction: Lysergic acid diethylamide acts as a partial agonist at serotonergic synapses in the CNS. A number of compounds have also been suggested to act as receptor blocking agents at serotonergic synapses but direct proof of these claims at the present time is lacking.

Site 5: Re-uptake: Considerable evidence now exists which suggests that serotonin may have its action terminated by being taken up into the presynaptic terminal. The tricyclic drugs with a tertiary nitrogen such as imipramine and amitryptyline appear to be potent inhibitors of this uptake mechanism.

Step 6: Monamine oxidase (MAO): Serotonin present in a free state within the presynaptic terminal can be degraded by the enzyme MAO which appears to be located in the outer membrane of mitochondria. Iproniazid is an effective inhibitor of MAO.

summarizes possible sites of drug interaction in a hypothetical serotonin synapse in the CNS.

## MULTICELLULAR BRAIN FUNCTIONS INVOLVING SEROTONIN

While we recognize that there is no single synaptic connection we can point to with certainty as being mediated by serotonin, there are, nevertheless, compelling data that serotonin-containing neurons are involved in certain multicellular functions of the brain.

## Temperature Regulation

In the chick, cat, dog, and monkey, intraventricular injection of microgram quantities of serotonin will produce profound elevation of body temperature. An elevation of body temperature also follows electrical stimulation of the rat raphe nuclei; this latter effect can be prevented if serotonin is previously depleted by either reserpine or p-chlorophenylalanine. The increase in body temperature could either be due to stimulation of mechanisms which elevate temperature or to inhibition of mechanisms which are able to prevent hyperthermia. In this regard, treatment with p-chlorophenylalanine, while removing brain serotonin, does not in itself produce hypothermia. Thus, while these experiments suggest that 5-HT may play some role in temperature regulation, they do not explain whether the effects are central or peripheral or whether they are either species specific or brain-region specific.

## Sensory Perception

We have already considered the possibilities that 5-HT may have some relationship to abnormal behavioral states such as those induced by tranquilizing or hallucinogenic drugs. In addition, animals treated with p-chlorophenylalanine were found to exhibit decreased motor activity, decreased emotional reactivity, and increased sensitivity to painful stimuli. The increased sensitivity to painful stimuli may be responsible for the observation that animals so treated are able to learn brightness discrimination more quickly since brightness discrimination is a somewhat painful stimulation; however, p-chlorophenylalanine treatment has no effect on the rate of learning of position discrimination.

When the raphe nuclei are stimulated electrically, animals fail to habituate to noise or repetitive sensory stimuli. This effect is similar to that seen during treatment with LSD as mentioned above. By whatever mechanism 5-HT-containing neurons are able to alter the perception or reaction to sensory stimuli, there appears to be a definite involvement, since blocking of serotonin has been reported to reduce the ability of rodents to become tolerant to chronic morphine injection.

*Sleep*

Several interrelated observations suggest that brain 5-HT is intimately involved in the mechanisms responsible for the various states of sleep. After either monoamine oxidase inhibition or intracerebral or intraventricular injection of 5-HT or 5-HTP, or after parenteral administration of 5-HTP there is electro-encephalographic evidence of increased time spent in slow-wave sleep. If brain serotonin content is drastically reduced either by electrical ablation of the raphe nuclei or by pretreatment with *p*-chlorophenylalanine, there is a marked decrease in the amount of slow-wave sleep time. The relative loss of sleep time appears proportional to the extent of the serotonin loss. On the other hand, electrical stimulation of the raphe nuclei does not induce slow-wave sleep and one wonders what mechanisms are required in order for the serotonin cells to complete those brain mechanisms responsible for the onset of slow-wave sleep. Direct microelectrode recordings have recently been made from identifiable neurons of the feline raphe nuclei during unrestrained waking and sleeping behavior. Neurons of the mesencephalic raphe under these conditions exhibit increased rates of discharge during slow-wave sleep, and fire very slowly while awake. The change in their discharge most frequently occurs after the cortical EEG changes from one sleep phase to another; thus, the changes in raphe discharge do not appear to cause the EEG phase shifts of sleep.

Furthermore, other brain amines appear relevant—at least pharmacologically—in sleep. Jouvet has suggested that the catecholamine and acetylcholine neuron participation may be most important in the transition from slow-wave sleep to rapid eye-movement sleep (also known as REM, paradoxical, or dream sleep). It has also been shown that gamma-hydroxybutyrate (see

Chapter 8) and certain short chain fatty acids will also induce sleep when injected parenterally under the right conditions. Thus the multicellular mechanisms controlling sleep phases do not belong exclusively to the 5-HT system of neurons.

*Summary*

In this chapter we have encountered one of the more striking examples of an intensively studied brain biogenic amine for which there is every reason to believe that it is an important synaptic transmitter. Still to be determined are the precise synaptic connections at which this substance accomplishes the transmission of information and the functional role these connections play in the over-all operation of the brain with respect to both affective and other multicellular interneuronal operations. With the exception of *p*-chlorophenylalanine, the drug that blocks serotonin synthesis at the tryptophan hydroxylase step, the central pharmacology of serotonin is poorly elucidated, particularly with respect to drugs that are specific postsynaptic blocking agents. The study of brain serotonin appears likely to be a most fruitful area for future research in the field of neuropsychopharmacology.

Aghajanian, G. K. (1972). LSD and CNS transmission. *Ann. Rev. Pharmacol. 12*, 157.

Aghajanian, G. K., and H. J. Haigler (1973). Studies on the activity of 5-HT neurons. *Proc. IVth Intl. Congr. Pharmacol. 4* (in press).

Barchas, J., and E. Usdin (1973). *Serotonin and Behavior*, Academic Press, New York (in press).

Baumgarten, H. G., A. Bjorklund, A. F. Holstein, and A. Nobin (1972). Chemical degeneration of indolamine axons in rat brain by 5,6-dihydroxytryptamine. *Z. Zellforsch. 129*, 256.

Bloom, F. E., B. J. Hoffer, G. R. Siggins, J. L. Barker, and R. A. Nicoll (1972). The effects of serotonin on central neurons: microionto-phoretic administration. *Fed. Proc. 31*, 97.

Falck, B., N.-A. Hillarp, G. Thieme, and A. Torp (1962). Fluorescence of catecholamines and related compounds condensed with formaldehyde. *J. Histochem. Cytochem. 10*, 348.

Felten, D. (1973). Localization of catecholamine and serotonin-containing cell bodies in the squirrel monkey brain. *J. Comp. Neurol.* (in press).

Garattini, S., P. A. Shore, E. Costa, and M. Sandler (1968). Biological role of indolealkylamine derivatives. *Adv. Pharmacol. 6A* and *6B*.

Giarman, N. J., and D. X. Freedman (1965). Biochemical aspects of the actions of psychotomimetic drugs. *Pharmacol. Rev. 17*, 1.

Green, A. R., S. H. Koslow, and E. Costa (1973). Identification and quantitation of a new indolealkylamine in rat hypothalamus. *Brain Res. 51*, 371.

Harvey, J. A., A. Heller, and R. Y. Moore (1963). The effect of unilateral and bilateral medial forebrain bundle lesions on brain serotonin. *J. Pharmacol. 140*, 103.

Jouvet, M. (1972). The role of monoamines and acetylcholine-containing neurons in the regulation of the sleep-waking cycle. *Ergeb. Physiol. 64*, 166.

Lovenberg, W. (1973). Tryptophan hydroxylase and serotonin synthesis in the brain. *Proc. IVth Intl. Congr. Pharmacol. 4* (in press).

Neff, N. H., R. C. Lin, S. H. Ngai, and E. Costa (1969). Turnover rate measurements of brain serotonin in unanesthetized rats. *Adv. Biochem. Psychopharmacol. 1*, 91.

Sims, K. L., and F. E. Bloom (1973). Rat brain 1-3,4-dihydroxyphenylalanine and 1-5-hydroxytryptophan decarboxylase activities: differential effect of 6-hydroxydopamine. *Brain Res. 49*, 165.

Wurtman, R. J., J. Axelrod, and D. E. Kelly (1968). *The Pineal*, Academic Press, New York.

# 8 | γ-Aminobutyric Acid, Glycine, and Glutamic Acid

## GABA

Synthesized in 1883, γ-aminobutyric acid (GABA) was known for many years as a product of microbial and plant metabolism. Not until 1950, however, did investigators identify GABA as a normal constituent of the mammalian central nervous system and find that no other mammalian tissue, with the exception of the retina, contains more than a mere trace of this material. Obviously, it was thought, a substance with such an unusual distribution must have some characteristic and unique physiological effects which might make it important for the function of the central nervous system. Almost twenty years later we still have no conclusive proof as to the role this compound plays in the mammalian central nervous system, although much evidence has accumulated supporting the hypothesis that it is an inhibitory transmitter.

### Distribution

In mammals, GABA has been detected in brain and spinal cord but not in peripheral nerve tissue such as sciatic nerve, splenic nerve, sympathetic ganglia, or in any other peripheral tissue such as liver, spleen, or heart. These findings give some idea of the uniqueness of the occurrence of GABA in the mammalian central nervous system. Like the monoamines, GABA also appears to have a discrete distribution within the central nervous system. However, unlike the monoamines, the concentration of GABA found in the central nervous system is in the order of μmoles/gm rather than nmoles/gm. It is interesting that brain also contains large amounts of glutamic acid (8-13 μmoles/gm), which is the main source of GABA. In the rat, the corpora quadrigemina and the diencephalic regions contain the highest levels of GABA, while

TABLE 8-1. Regional Distribution of GABA in Monkey Brain
Data taken from S. Fahn and L. J. Côté (1968).

| | Region of brain | n | μmoles/g frozen tissue ± S.E.M. |
|---|---|---|---|
| Highest | substantia nigra | 4 | 9.70 ± 0.63 |
| | globus pallidus | 4 | 9.54 ± 0.91 |
| | hypothalamus | 4 | 6.19 ± 0.13 |
| High | inferior colliculus | 4 | 4.70 ± 0.29 |
| | dentate nucleus | 3 | 4.30 ± 0.47 |
| | superior colliculus | 3 | 4.19 ± 1.09 |
| | periaqueductal gray | 3 | 4.02 ± 0.56 |
| Medium | putamen | 4 | 3.62 ± 0.21 |
| | pontine tegmentum | 4 | 3.34 ± 0.43 |
| | caudate nucleus | 4 | 3.20 ± 0.18 |
| | medial thalamus | 4 | 3.00 ± 0.14 |
| Low | lateral thalamus | 4 | 2.68 ± 0.09 |
| | occipital cortex | 4 | 2.68 ± 0.23 |
| | anterior thalamus | 4 | 2.50 ± 0.23 |
| | medullary tegmentum | 4 | 2.27 ± 0.22 |
| | inferior olivary nucleus | 4 | 2.25 ± 0.15 |
| | frontal cortex | 4 | 2.10 ± 0.01 |
| | motor cortex | 4 | 2.09 ± 0.10 |
| | cerebellar cortex (not pure gray) | 4 | 2.03 ± 0.23 |
| Lowest | centrum semiovale (pure white) | 4 | 0.31 ± 1.0 |

much lower concentrations are found in whole cerebral hemispheres, the pons, and medulla; white matter contains relatively low concentrations of GABA. Recently, the discrete localization of GABA in the brain of anesthetized monkeys has been determined by Fahn and Côté and by DeFeudis *et al*. Some of this data is summarized in Table 8-1. It should be noted that endogenous levels of GABA increase rapidly post mortem: a 30 to 45 per cent increase in GABA occurs within two minutes after death in the rat if the tissue is not instantly frozen *in situ*. The origin of this sudden increase is unknown, but it seems quite unlikely that it could be solely explained by *de novo* synthesis.

Progressive increases in GABA levels and in glutamic acid decarboxylase activity appear to occur in various regions of the brain during development. The high levels of GABA found in the various regions of the brain of the Rhesus monkey appear to correlate well with the activity of glutamate decarboxylase, the enzyme responsible for the conversion of L-glutamate to GABA. This is not the case for the degradative enzyme GABA-transaminase, since the globus pallidus and the substantia nigra, which have the highest concentration of GABA, have a relatively low transaminase activity. Yet there does not appear to be a consistent inverse relationship between GABA concentration and transaminase activity. Thus, some areas of brain, such as the dentate nucleus and the inferior colliculus, which have relatively high concentrations of GABA also have large amounts of transaminase activity.

Since GABA does not easily penetrate the blood-brain barrier, it is difficult if not impossible to increase the brain concentrations of GABA by peripheral administration, unless one alters the blood-brain barrier. Some investigators have tried to circumvent this problem by the administration of GABA-lactam (2-pyrrolidinone) to animals in the hope that this less polar and more lipid soluble compound would penetrate more easily into the brain and be hydrolyzed to yield GABA. Although the idea seems plausible, it does not succeed: the GABA-lactam that reaches the central nervous system is not hydrolyzed to any extent.

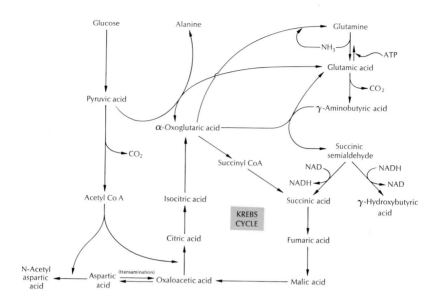

FIGURE 8-1. Interrelationship between γ-aminobutyric acid and carbohydrate metabolism.

## Metabolism

There are three primary enzymes involved in the metabolism of GABA prior to its entry into the Krebs cycle. The relative activity of enzymes involved in the degradation of GABA suggest that, similar to monoamines, they play only a minor role in the termination of the action of any neurally released GABA.

Figure 8-1 outlines the metabolism of GABA and its relationship to the Krebs cycle and carbohydrate metabolism. As mentioned previously, GABA is formed by the α-decarboxylation of L-glutamic acid, a reaction catalyzed by glutamic acid decarboxylase, an enzyme which occurs uniquely in the mammalian central nervous system and retinal tissue. The precursor of GABA, L-glutamic acid can be formed from α-oxoglutarate by transamination or reaction with ammonia. GABA is intimately related to the oxidative metabolism of carbohydrates in the central nervous system by means of a "shunt" involving its production from glutamate, its transamination with $\alpha$-oxoglutarate by GABA-$\alpha$-oxoglutarate transaminase (GABA-T) yielding succinic semialdehyde and regenerating glutamate, and its entry into the Krebs cycle as succinic acid via the oxidation of succinic semialdehyde by succinic semialdehyde dehydrogenase. In essence then the "shunt" bypasses the normal oxidative metabolism involving the enzymes $\alpha$-oxoglutarate dehydrogenase and succinyl thiokinase.

From a metabolic standpoint, the significance of the "shunt" is unknown; energetically at least it is less efficient than direct oxidation through the Krebs cycle (3 ATP equivalents versus 3 ATP + 1 GTP for the Krebs cycle). Experimentally, it has been quite difficult to make an adequate assessment of the quantitative significance of the "shunt" in the oxidation of $\alpha$-oxoglutarate *in vivo*. Studies with [14]C-labeled glucose both *in vivo* and *in vitro* have indicated that the carbon chain of GABA can be derived from glucose. Therefore, in some cases the incorporation of radioactivity into the "shunt" metabolites following the injection of uniformly labeled [14]C-glucose has been used to assess the functional aspects of this "shunt." However, these experiments are somewhat inconclusive since they do not necessarily indicate the rate of flux through this pathway. Some relatively indirect experiments have given results suggesting that about 10 to 40 per cent of the total brain metabolism may funnel through this "shunt."

### Glutamic Acid Decarboxylase (GAD)

GAD is the enzyme responsible for the conversion of L-glutamic acid to GABA. At the present time no convincing evidence has been gathered to indicate that significant amounts of GABA are formed by reactions other than the decarboxylation of L-glutamic acid. No reversal of this reaction has been demonstrable either *in vivo* or *in vitro*. In mammalian organisms this relatively specific decarboxylase is found only in the central nervous system, where it occurs in higher concentrations in the gray matter. In general, the localization of this enzyme in mammalian brain correlates quite well with the GABA content. So far this enzyme has been purified about 200-fold from mouse brain. It has a pH optimum of about 6.5, requires pyridoxal phosphate, and is inhibited by various anions. This inhibition by anions may be interesting from a physiological standpoint. The possibility has been raised that variations in the chloride concentration at a given nerve ending could control GABA formation. Although there is no evidence of wide variations in chloride content under normal physiological conditions, it is of interest that in snail brain the D cells (depolarized by acetylcholine) and the H cells (hyperpolarized by acetylcholine) have different chloride contents. In fact, the D cells have an internal chloride content about three times that of the H cells. The GAD isolated and purified from lobster inhibitory nerve is inhibited by concentrations of GABA (0.1 M) similar to the actual endogenous concentrations found in the inhibitory fiber. This raises the possibility that at least in the lobster inhibitory neuron GABA may control its own formation via product inhibition of GAD and thus provide a homeostatic mechanism for maintenance of steady state levels of GABA during periods of altered utilization of transmitter. However, the GAD isolated from mammalian brain does not seem to be inhibited by GABA, and thus it is unlikely that such a regulatory mechanism occurs in mammalian brain. Both the invertebrate and the mammalian brain enzyme require pyridoxal phosphate as a cofactor and thus are inhibited by a variety of pyridoxal antagonists including various carbonyl trapping agents such as amino-oxyacetic acid and various hydrazines. Potassium ion and $\beta$-mercaptoethanol are essential for activity of the purified lobster enzyme.

Recently another mammalian GAD (type 2) has been described. This enzyme differs from the brain GAD (type 1) in that it is insensitive to inhibition by chloride ions and is stimulated rather than inhibited by certain carbonyl trapping agents. In contrast to the brain GAD, this enzyme in addition to being found in

CNS white matter is also found in non-neuronal tissue such as kidney and human glial cells grown in culture. However, the existence of GAD type 2 has been questioned since the product of the reaction has not been convincingly demonstrated.

## GABA-Transaminase (GABA-T)

GABA-T, unlike the decarboxylase, has a wide tissue distribution. Therefore, although GABA cannot be formed to any extent outside the central nervous system, exogenous GABA can be rapidly metabolized by both central and peripheral tissue. However, since endogenous GABA has not been detected in cerebrospinal fluid or blood it is unlikely that it ever leaves the brain intact. The brain transaminase has a pH optimum of 8.2 and also requires pyridoxal phosphate. It appears that the coenzyme is more tightly bound to this enzyme than it is to GAD. The brain ratio of GABA-T/GAD activity is almost always greater than one. Sulfhydryl reagents tend to decrease GABA-T activity, suggesting that this enzyme requires the integrity of one or more sulfhydryl groups for optimal activity. The transamination of GABA catalyzed by GABA-T is a reversible reaction, so if a metabolic source of succinic semialdehyde were made available it would be theoretically possible to form GABA by the reversal of this reaction. However, as indicated below, this does not appear to be the case *in vivo* in normal or experimental conditions so far investigated.

Recent studies with more sophisticated cell fractionation techniques and electron microscopic monitoring of the fractions obtained have borne out the original claims that both GAD and GABA-T are particulate to some extent. GAD was found associated with the synaptosome fraction, whereas the GABA-T was largely associated with mitochondria. Further studies on the mitochondrial distribution of GABA-T have suggested that the mitochondria released from synaptosomes have less activity than the crude unpurified mitochondrial fraction, and it has been inferred that the mitochondria within nerve endings have little GABA-T activity. This finding has led to the speculation that GABA is metabolized largely at extraneuronal intercellular sites or in the postsynaptic neurons.

## Succinic Semialdehyde Dehydrogenase (SSADH)

Brain succinic semialdehyde dehydrogenase (SSADH) has a high substrate specificity and can be distinguished from the nonspecific aldehyde dehydrogenase found in brain. The enzyme purified from human brain has a pH optimum of about 9.2 and quite a low Michaelis constant ($K_m$) for succinic semialdehyde of $5.3 \times 10^{-6}$. SSADH from rat brain has a similarly low $K_m$ for succinic semialdehyde of $7.8 \times 10^{-5}$ and for NAD of $5 \times 10^{-5}$. The high activity of this enzyme and the low Michaelis constant, which allow the enzyme to function effectively at low substrate concentrations, probably account for the fact that succinic semialdehyde (SSA) has not even been detected as an endogenous metabolite in neural tissue despite the active metabolism of GABA *in vivo*. In contrast to SSADH isolated from bacterial sources where NADP is several times more active as a cofactor than NAD, the enzyme from monkey and human brain demonstrates a specificity for NAD as a cofactor. The regional distribution of this enzyme has been studied in human brain and found to parallel the distribution of GABA-T activity, although the dehydrogenase is about 1.5 times as active. The greatest activity was found in the hypothalamus, basal ganglia, cortical gray matter, and mesencephalic tegmentum. SSADH also has a marked heat activation at 38°C, and Pitts suggested that its activity *in vivo* might be regulated by temperature such that fever might result in an increased flux through the GABA shunt. This appears unlikely, however, since this step is usually not considered to be rate limiting in the conversion of GABA to succinic acid, and thus small changes in its activity would not be reflected in an over-all change in GABA metabolism. A sensitive and specific assay for SSADH is based on the fluorescence of NADH formed in the conversion of succinic semialdehyde to succinic acid. This method is sensitive enough to assay samples as small as 0.05 μg of freeze-dried brain tissue.

Since GABA's rise to popularity, the literature has been inundated with reports purporting to demonstrate that many pharmacological and physiological effects can be ascribed to and correlated well with changes in the brain levels of this substance. Since both GAD and GABA-T are dependent on the coenzyme pyridoxal phosphate it is not surprising that pharmacological agents or pathological conditions affecting this coenzyme can cause alterations in the GABA content of the brain. Epileptiform seizure can be produced by a lack of this coenzyme or by its inactivation. Conditions of this sort also lead to a reduction in GABA levels, since GAD appears to be preferentially inhibited over the transaminase, presumably due to the fact that GAD has a lower affinity for the coenzyme than does GABA-T. A diet deficient in vitamin $B_6$ in infants can lead to seizures that respond successfully to treatment consisting of addition of pyridoxine to the diet. However, it must be remembered that many other enzymes, including some of those involved in the biosynthesis of other bioactive substances, are also pyridoxal-dependent enzymes. A number of observations, in fact, indicate that there is no simple correlation between GABA content and convulsive activity. Administration of a variety of hydrazides to animals has uniformly resulted in the production of repetitive seizures following a rather prolonged latent period. The finding that the hydrazide-induced seizures could be prevented by parenteral administration of various forms of vitamin $B_6$ led to the suggestion that some enzyme system requiring pyridoxal phosphate as a coenzyme was being inhibited and that the decrease in the activity of this enzyme was somehow related to the production of the seizures observed. At this time attention focused on GABA and GAD because of their unique occurrence in the central nervous system and because GAD had been shown to be inhibited by carbonyl trapping agents *in vitro*. The hydrazide-induced seizures were accompanied by substantial decreases in the levels of GABA and reductions in GAD activity in various areas of the brain studied. (This decrease in GABA produced by thiosemicarbazide is now believed to be due to a decrease in the rapid post-mortem increase in GABA mentioned previously.) The direct demonstration of the reversal of the action of the convulsant hydrazides by GABA itself proved to be difficult, due to the lack of ability of GABA to pass the blood-brain barrier in adult mammalian organisms. However, a preferential inhibition of GABA-T could be achieved *in vivo* with carbonyl reagents such as hydroxylamine ($NH_2OH$) or amino-oxyacetic acid which resulted in an increase in GABA levels (up to 500 per cent of control) in the central nervous system. However, although these agents caused a decrease in the susceptibility to the seizures induced by some agents, such as metrazole, they did not exert any protective effect against the hydrazide-induced convulsions, even though they prevented the depletion of GABA and in some cases even increased the GABA levels above the controls. In fact, administration of very high doses of only amino-oxyacetic acid instead of producing the normally observed sedation caused some seizure activity in spite of the extremely high brain levels of GABA.

An interesting finding with amino-oxyacetic acid is that administration of this compound to a strain of genetically spastic mice in a single dose of 5-15 mg/kg results in a marked improvement of their symptomatology for 12 to 24 hours. This improvement is associated with an increase in GABA levels, but the GABA level increases with a similar time course and to the same extent as in normal control mice. All studies to date indicate that the principal genetic defect in these mice is not in the operation of the GABA system. However, the drug-induced increase in GABA may serve to quell an excess of or imbalance in excitatory input in some unknown area of the central nervous system.

Hydrazinopropionic acid has recently been described as a potent inhibitor of GABA-T. It has been suggested that this compound inhibits GABA-T because of its close similarity to GABA with respect to structural configuration, molecular size, and molecular charge distribution. Its inhibitory action cannot be reversed by the addition of pyridoxal phosphate. Hydrazinopropionic acid is about 1000 times more potent than aminooxyacetic acid in inhibiting mouse brain transaminase.

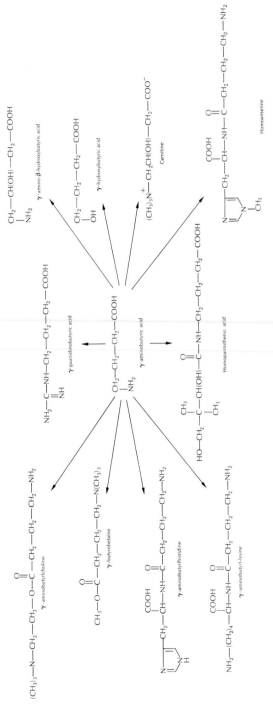

FIGURE 8-2. Possible alternate metabolic pathways for γ-aminobutyric acid.

*Alternate Metabolic Pathways*

In addition to undergoing transamination and subsequently entering the Krebs cycle, GABA can apparently undergo various other transformations in the central nervous system, forming a number of compounds whose importance, and in some cases natural occurrence, has not been conclusively established. Figure 7-2 depicts a variety of derivatives for which GABA may serve as a precursor. Perhaps the simplest of these metabolic conversions is the reduction of succinic semialdehyde (a product of GABA transamination) to γ-hydroxybutyrate (GHB). The transformation of GABA to GHB has been demonstrated in rat brain both *in vivo* and *in vitro*. In addition, the natural occurrence of GHB has been established by means of gas chromatography. Rat brain contains about 2 nmoles/gm while guinea pig brain contains almost twice this concentration. Among brain metabolites γ-hydroxybutyrate is rather unique in that this compound possesses anesthetic properties. Whether or not this compound plays any role in the normal sleep processes or in the pathogenesis of sleep disorders remains to be determined. GHB also has an interesting interrelationship with the catecholamines in that exogenously administered GHB or γ-butyrolactone (GBL) in doses which produce "sleep" (i.e. loss of righting reflex) causes a large increase in brain dopamine content with little or no effect on brain norepinephrine, serotonin, or GABA. This increase in brain dopamine induced by GHB appears to be largely a result of the ability of this agent to block impulse flow in dopaminergic neurons.

Several conflicting reports concerning the natural occurrence of γ-amino-β-hydroxybutyric acid (GABOB) in mammalian brain have appeared in the literature. Some investigators claim that GABOB occurs in mammalian brain in concentrations as high as four μmoles per gram. Others have reported its presence in much smaller amounts or its total absence. The most careful studies employing automated amino acid analysis and two-dimensional paper chromatography have indicated that GABOB is either absent in rat brain or present in amounts less than 0.01 μmoles per gram. However, despite the fact that little or no GABOB is present in brain, many electrophysiological investigations have been conducted to determine its possible action as a neuro-inhibitory substance. This compound has been claimed by some to block experimentally induced convulsions in animals when administered topically to the brain or even systemically. Also some investigators have claimed that GABOB is effective clinically in preventing and alleviating epileptic seizures. When administered iontophoretically to single neurons in the cerebral cortex, GABOB exerts a depressant effect comparable in potency to GABA. On the crayfish stretch receptor neuron, GABOB is only about one-half as potent as GABA.

γ-aminobutyrylcholine was detected in 1958 by paper chromatography in mammalian brain. More recently, a more rigorous identification has been made by Kewitz, who estimated the concentration in rat brain to be about 80 nmoles/gm. This choline ester appears to be resistant to hydrolysis by acetylcholinesterase while butyrocholinesterase has some limited capacity to hydrolyze this substance at a rather slow rate. In addition, this ester does not appear to undergo transamination with α-oxoglutarate as does the parent compound—GABA. Although it produces a potent and prolonged depressant effect on the neuromuscular junction, its effects on the central nervous system have not been extensively studied. When the action of γ-aminobutyrylcholine was studied by means of iontophoresis onto cerebral cortical neurons there was relatively little depressant activity. In fact, the action was less than that of γ-aminobutyrobetaine, which is itself only a weak depressant. Curiously, when γ-aminobutyrylcholine was applied topically to the cerebral cortex its depressant potency was similar to that of GABA. In fact it is about 1000 times as active as GABA in suppressing metrazole-induced spikes in the EEG recording of the mammalian cortex. It has both a depressant and an excitatory action on Renshaw cells in the spinal cord.

γ-butyrobetaine is a substance which has been known for many years to be present in tissues obtained from snakes and eels but only recently has it been suggested to occur in mammalian tissue. This compound has been only tentatively identified in the mammalian central nervous system in a complex with coenzyme A. Pharmacologically, the action of γ-butyrobetaine resembles to some extent that of acetylcholine, except that it is substantially less potent and has a more prolonged action on tissues such as the superior cervical ganglion, ileum, and the neuromuscular junction. γ-butyrobetaine is pharmacologically inactive when iontophoresed onto cortical neurons.

γ-guanidinobutyric acid also appears to be a normal metabolite of mammalian brain and could act as a source of GABA by means of transamidination. This compound can inhibit the crayfish stretch receptor but is somewhat less potent than GABA in this respect. A few drops of a 1 per cent solution applied topically markedly augments the evoked potentials of the cerebral cortex while it depresses the cerebellar response.

γ-aminobutyrylhistidine (homocarnosine) has been reported to occur in beef brain (10-25 $\mu$g/gm), dog and cat brain (1.2 $\mu$g/gm), human brain (80 $\mu$g/gm), and frog brain (240 $\mu$g/gm), but the biological significance of this compound remains unknown.

Acetylcarnitine and carnitine have also been suggested to be normal metabolites of mammalian brain, although their occurrence is by no means restricted to this tissue. The esters of carnitine possess acetylcholine-like activity in a number of biological preparations.

It is not surprising that γ-aminobutyryl-lysine has recently been identified as a normal constituent of the rabbit central nervous system, since earlier studies had indicated that the enzyme which catalyzes the synthesis of carnosine and homocarnosine also forms peptides of GABA and various basic amino acids. However, although this compound seems to occur exclusively in the central nervous system, it does not appear to have any discrete regional localization. Degradation of this peptide appears to be catalyzed by a different enzyme than carnosinase, which usually attacks peptides containing an imidazole in the terminal carboxyl position. An enzyme catalyzing the degradation of γ-aminobutyryl-lysine and other peptides with arginine, lysine, and ornithine in their carboxyl terminals has been found in brain.

## Neurotransmitter Role

Quite a strong case can be made for a transmitter role for GABA at inhibitory nerve endings to the muscle or to stretch receptor neurons in crustacea. The evidence can be summarized as follows:

1. Externally applied GABA duplicates the effects of inhibitory nerve stimulation at the crustacean neuromuscular junction as well as at other crustacean synapses.

2. Both exogenous GABA and the endogenous inhibitory transmitter substance when in contact with postsynaptic membrane or receptor site cause this membrane to become more permeable to chloride ion. This increase in chloride permeability in both cases can be blocked by picrotoxin and bicuculline, potent GABA receptor blockers.

3. GABA appears to be the most potent inhibitory compound extractable from the lobster nervous system.

4. Inhibitory axons and cell bodies in the lobster nervous system have a much higher content of GABA than excitatory axons or cell bodies, the GABA ratio found being on the order of $100 : 1$. The endogenous GABA content of the inhibitory axon is approximately $0.1M$.

5. The enzymes necessary for the formation and destruction of GABA are present in the inhibitory axon and cell body.

6. A specific GABA uptake mechanism, which could be involved in transmitter inactivation, analogous to the norepinephrine system, has been described in the crayfish stretch receptor and the lobster nerve-muscle preparation. However, it is not known if the uptake is primarily into presynaptic nerve terminals.

7. Most recently it has been demonstrated that GABA is released by the lobster nerve-muscle preparation during

stimulation of the inhibitory axons. This release was shown to be frequency dependent. Moreover, stimulation of the excitatory nerve to the same muscle does not liberate GABA. Also, GABA release induced by stimulation of the inhibitory fibers can be blocked by lowering the $Ca^{++}$ content of the medium, which also blocks neuromuscular transmission.

## Neurotransmitter Role in the Mammalian Central Nervous System

The action of GABA in the crustacean nervous system has sometimes been used as indirect evidence that this substance also functions as a neurotransmitter in the mammalian central nervous system. While there is no doubt that these speculations have served to generate a great deal of interest, the observations made in the crustacean nervous system cannot substitute for data on the events taking place in the mammalian nervous system.

The evidence from the central nervous system to support a role of GABA as an inhibitory transmitter is still somewhat deficient. With substances such as the amino acids, which may play a dual role (both in metabolism and as neurotransmitters), it is only to be expected that it will be more difficult to obtain conclusive evidence as to their role as neurotransmitters. The elementary criteria for identification of a compound as a putative transmitter have already been mentioned. In short, the agent in question must be produced, stored, released, exert its appropriate action, and be removed from its site of action. There is sufficient evidence for the production, storage, and pharmacological activity of GABA consistent with its suggestive role as an inhibitory transmitter, but it has not yet been possible to demonstrate an association of GABA with specific inhibitory pathways in the cortex. Until recently there was also no evidence that GABA could be released from mammalian brain under physiological conditions. Several reports now claim to have demonstrated the spontaneous release of GABA from the surface of the brain. However, only one group of investigators has claimed that the amount of GABA released from the cortex is dependent upon the activity of the brain. This group has found that in cats showing an aroused EEG, either following cervical cord section or in awake animals receiving local anesthesia, small amounts of GABA will leak out of the cerebral cortex and can be recovered by a superfusion technique (cortical cup) provided the pia-arachnoid membrane has been punctured. This release of GABA into cortical cups occurs about three times more rapidly from the brains of cats showing an EEG sleep-like pattern with marked spindle activity following midbrain section than in cats showing an EEG awake pattern. When a continuous waking state was maintained by periodic stimulation of the brain stem reticular formation, no measurable amount of GABA could be found in the perfusates. Recently, Iversen and coworkers have demonstrated that GABA is released from the surface of the posterior lateral gyri of cats during periods of cortical inhibition produced by either stimulation of the ipsilateral geniculate or by direct stimulation of the cortex. DeFeudis, Delgado, and Roth have been able to demonstrate the release of newly synthesized GABA (and other amino acids) from

FIGURE 8-3. Amino acid profile and semi-logarithmic plots of the distribution of radioactivity after perfusion of the right caudate nucleus of a Rhesus monkey with $^{14}$C-glucose. A volume of 2.28 ml was collected every minute and a 1.5 ml aliquot was counted for radioactivity; 29 mg of caudate nucleus and its corresponding perfusate collected over ½ hr (0.5 ml) were analyzed. Buffer charges and elution time are indicated. Since the column of resin used for the perfusate was 2 cm shorter than that used for the extract, GABA was eluted sooner in this analysis but coincided exactly with the ninhydrin positive peak. Abbreviations: MSO, methionine sulfoxide; ASP, aspartate; GLN, glutamine; ASPN, asparagine; SER, serine; GLU, glutamate; PRO, proline; GLY, glycine; ALA, α-alanine; VAL, valine; ILE, isoleucine; LEU, leucine; TYR, tyrosine; PHE, phenylalanine; GABA, γ-aminobutyric acid. (Unpublished photograph, data in DeFeudis, Delgado, and Roth, 1970.)

deep brain nuclei of monkeys such as the amygdala and caudate nucleus, using push-pull cannulas. As yet, however, this release has not been correlated with brain activity.

Figure 8-3 illustrates an automated amino acid analysis of an extract from a caudate nucleus perfused with uniformly labeled

[14]C-glucose and the perfusate obtained from this structure. This technique has the advantage that it provides a rigorous establishment of the identity of the amino acids collected as well as enabling the detection of very minute amounts of these substances. When GABA is applied iontophoretically to Deiters' neurons it induces IPSP-like changes and therefore mimics the action of the inhibitory transmitter released from axon terminals of the Purkinje cells. GABA is also known to be concentrated in Purkinje cells which exert a monosynaptic inhibitory effect on neurons of Deiters' nucleus. Recently Obata and Takeda observed that stimulation of the cerebellum, which presumably activates the Purkinje cell axons, which have their terminals in cerebellar subcortical nuclei adjacent to the fourth ventricle, induces about a threefold increase in the amount of GABA released into the ventricular perfusate. However, the extremely high voltage employed, the relatively crude perfusion system, and the lack of critical identification of GABA make the significance of these otherwise interesting observations on release somewhat difficult to interpret, although they are consistent with the hypothesis that GABA is an inhibitory transmitter in the particular pathway.

In addition, other recent experiments have indicated that labeled GABA can be released from brain slices by electrical stimulation or by the addition of high potassium to the incubation medium. However, one should bear in mind that all the above-mentioned release experiments are somewhat gross in nature and do not provide evidence with regard to the neuronal system involved in the release of GABA or even if this release is in any way associated with an inhibitory synaptic event. In fact, at the present time no suitable test system in the CNS has been developed which will be as appropriate as the lobster nerve-muscle preparation. The student is advised against holding his intellectual breath until it has.

Most of the investigations analyzing the mechanism of GABA's depressive action on the central nervous system have been conducted on spinal cord motor neurons. Until quite recently GABA had not shown much evidence of closely mimicking the inhibitory transmitter. In fact, only a few years ago Curtis and his associates discounted the hypothesis that GABA might be the main inhibitory transmitter in the mammalian central nervous system. They noted that the action of GABA iontophoresed onto spinal neurons differed significantly from that of the inhibitory transmitter; whereas natural postsynaptic inhibition was associated with membrane hyperpolarization, experiments with coaxial pipettes failed to detect any hyperpolarization of motor neurons during the administration of GABA. Since at that time there was no evidence that GABA had a hyperpolarizing action in other parts of the central nervous system, Curtis concluded that GABA could not be the main central inhibitory transmitter. Recently, other investigators have demonstrated that in the cortical neurons of the cat GABA imitates the action of the cortical inhibitory transmitter at least qualitatively; it usually raises the membrane potential and increases conductance of cortical neurons, just like the normal inhibitory synaptic mechanism. When the latter inhibitory effect is artificially reversed by the administration of chloride into the neuron, the action of GABA is also reversed in a similar way. Similar results have been obtained on neurons in Deiters' nucleus. Therefore, at least as far as the cortex and Deiters' nucleus are concerned, there appears to be much support for the hypothesis that GABA is an inhibitory transmitter. Furthermore, the "negative data" obtained previously by Curtis have been criticized on conceptual and technical grounds.

There appears to be no pharmacologically sensitive mechanism for the rapid destruction of GABA similar to the cholinesterase mechanism for destruction of acetylcholine. Thus aminooxyacetic acid or hydroxylamine given intravenously or iontophoresed does not appear to prolong significantly the duration of action of iontophoretically applied GABA. The exception is Deiters' nucleus, where the hyperpolarization produced by GABA on the neurons in Deiters' nucleus and the IPSP are prolonged in both cases by hydroxylamine, an agent of dubious pharmacological specificity. No functional re-uptake mechanism for GABA within a mammalian system has been conclusively demonstrated either. However, GABA is actively and efficiently taken up by brain slices and this implies that some uptake phenomena are functional in the intact brain for recycling GABA and terminating its action. This mechanism could also explain why it has been difficult to collect GABA released from neural tissue. Unfortunately, no drug has been discovered which will effectively block the uptake of GABA into nervous tissue without exerting a number of other unwanted pharmacological actions. Therefore, it is difficult to evaluate the functional significance of this uptake mechanism. The development of a selective inhibitor of GABA uptake might prove to be quite useful in the study of GABA systems in the CNS.

Another possible fruitful area of approach is to look for a specific inhibitor of GAD so GABA could be depleted selectively from the central nervous system. At present no really specific inhibitors for GAD have been developed that can inhibit this enzyme *in vivo* without also inhibiting GABA-T and a variety of other B6-dependent enzymes. Another real advance would be the development of a histochemical method for the visualization of GABA at the electron microscope level.

Equally important for the study of this system would be the availability of specific pharmacological antagonists of GABA. Until recently picrotoxin was the best substance available for antagonizing the actions of GABA. In crustacean muscle preparations picrotoxin appears to block selectively the action of GABA as well as the natural inhibitory transmitter. However, in general the degree of specificity of picrotoxin in mammalian systems is not good enough to establish it as a selective antagonist of GABA

---

FIGURE 8-4. Schematic illustration of a GABAergic neuron indicating possible sites of drug action.

Site 1: Enzymatic synthesis: Glutamic acid decarboxylase (GAD-I) is inhibited by a number of various hydrazines. These agents appear to act primarily as pyridoxal antagonists and are therefore very nonspecific inhibitors. L-glutamate-γ-hydrazide and allylglycine are more selective inhibitors of GAD-I but these agents are also not entirely specific in their effects on GAD-I.

Site 2: Release: GABA release appears to be calcium dependent. At present no selective inhibitors of GABA release have been found.

Site 3: Interaction with postsynaptic receptor: Bicuculline and picrotoxin block the action of GABA at postsynaptic receptors. 3-aminopropane sulfonic acid and the hallucinogenic isoxazole derivative, muscimol, appear to be effective GABA agonists at postsynaptic receptors.

Site 4: Re-uptake: In brain GABA appears to be actively taken up into presynaptic endings by a sodium-dependent mechanism. A number of compounds will inhibit this uptake mechanism such as 2-hydroxy-GABA, p-chloromercuriphenyl sulfonic acid, chlorpromazine, and imipramine but these agents are not specific in their inhibitory effects.

Site 5: Metabolism: GABA is metabolized primarily by transamination by GABA-transaminase (GABA-T) which appears to be localized primarily in mitochondria. Amino-oxyacetic acid is an effective inhibitor of GABA-T.

at a given site. Recently, the alkaloid bicuculline has been shown to be a more specific inhibitor of GABA's action in the mammalian CNS. Bicuculline is also an effective inhibitor of GABA's action at the crayfish stretch receptor.

So far it has been difficult to determine if any physiological or even pharmacological alteration of animal behavior produces alterations in the function of the GABA system in the intact animal. This is primarily because a simple and reliable technique has not been developed for the measurement of GABA turnover *in vivo*. Thus we are limited to looking at changes in the brain levels of GABA in order to glean some evidence concerning the activity of this system. Since the brain undoubtedly has many homeostatic mechanisms for the maintenance of GABA levels under widely varying conditions of activity, it would seem that changes in the activity of the GABA system, at least within the physiological range, would not necessarily lead to substantial changes in GABA concentration within the brain. Thus, development of any technique which could reliably evaluate the turnover of GABA *in vivo* would undoubtedly add to a better understanding of the functional importance of GABA in the central nervous system.

It seems likely that two recently reported cytochemical procedures may eventually permit an even more detailed anatomical description of GABA pathways in the CNS through localization of succinic semialdehyde dehydrogenase and through fluorescence histochemical study of GABA. Once the anatomy of the GABA-containing neuronal systems in the mammalian CNS is clearly defined it should be possible to learn a great deal more about the functional aspects of these systems. Figure 8-4 depicts possible sites of drug interaction in a hypothetical GABAergic synapse.

## GLYCINE

### *As an Inhibitory Transmitter*

Our knowledge of the metabolism of glycine in nervous tissue is still quite rudimentary despite the fact that the process has been

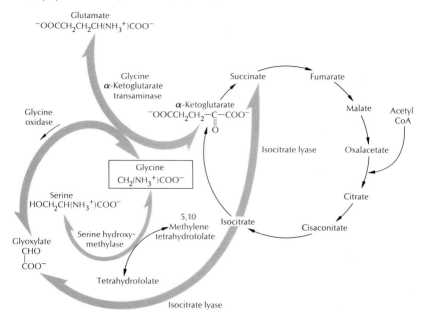

FIGURE 8-5. Possible metabolic routes for the formation and degradation of glycine by nervous tissue. (Modified after Roberts and Hammerschlag. In: *Basic Neurochemistry*, Little, Brown, 1972, p. 151.)

studied quite extensively in other tissues. For example, we still do not know whether biosynthesis is important for the maintenance of glycine levels in the spinal cord or whether the neurons depend upon the uptake and accumulation of preformed glycine. As indicated in Figure 8-5, glycine can be formed from serine by a reversible folate dependent reaction catalyzed by the enzyme, serine trans-hydroxy-methylase. Serine itself can also be formed in nerve tissue from glucose via the intermediates 3-phosphoglycerate and 3-phosphoserine. It is also conceivable that glycine might be formed from glyoxylate via a transaminase reaction with glutamate. Not only is our knowledge of the metabolism of glycine in nervous tissue minimal but at the present time only scanty information is available on the factors regulating the concentration of glycine in the CNS. Glycine in the spinal cord is labeled only slowly from radioactive glucose via one of the glycolytic intermediates indicated in Figure 8-5. It is also possible to label glycine by administration of labeled glyoxylate, which is readily transaminated to glycine by nervous tissue.

Substantial evidence now exists which indicates that glycine may play a role as an inhibitory transmitter in the mammalian spinal cord. From the evidence available we will try to assess how well this compound fulfills the criteria necessary to categorize this substance as a central nervous system inhibitory transmitter. First, we can say that this amino acid is found in relatively high concentrations in the spinal cord compared with other amino acids. Table 8-2 illustrates the occurrence of glycine and other free amino acids in the spinal cord, and from these data it is apparent that glycine is more concentrated in the spinal gray matter than in the spinal white matter. The concentration found in the spinal

TABLE 8-2. Amino Acid Concentration of Cat Spinal Cord and Roots ($\mu moles/g$)

| Amino acids | Spinal gray | Dorsal root | Ventral root |
|---|---|---|---|
| Alanine | 0.62 | 0.36 | 0.30 |
| Arginine | 0.14 | 0.07 | 0.06 |
| Aspartate | 2.14 | 0.79 | 1.13 |
| Cystathionine | 3.02 | 0.02 | 0.01 |
| GABA | 0.84 | Trace | Trace |
| Glutamate | 4.48 | 3.33 | 2.09 |
| Glutamine | 5.48 | 1.46 | 1.10 |
| Glycine | 4.47 | 0.28 | 0.32 |
| Leucine | 0.16 | 0.06 | 0.05 |
| Lysine | 0.16 | 0.07 | 0.05 |
| Methyl-histamine | — | — | — |
| Serine | 0.41 | 0.32 | 0.23 |
| Threonine | 0.21 | 0.18 | 0.15 |

Data taken from: M. H. Aprison and R. Werman (1968).

gray matter is much higher than the level in whole brain or spinal roots. This high level of glycine in the ventral horn, together with the comparatively low content in ventral root fibers, initially suggested that glycine may be associated with the inhibitory interneurons, and subsequently this was shown to be the case. From iontophoretic studies the compounds in Table 8-2 can be divided into four main groups.

1. Excitatory    glutamate, aspartate
2. Inhibitory    GABA, glycine, alanine, cystathionine, and serine
3. Inactive      glutamine, leucine, threonine, and lysine
4. Untested      arginine and methyl histidine

Of the amino acids in group two, cystathionine and serine appear to have a weaker and relatively sluggish action on spinal neurons compared with that of GABA and glycine. Therefore, in view of the distribution and the relative inhibitory potency of the compounds in this group, it was suggested by Aprison and Werman that GABA and glycine were the most likely candidates for spinal inhibitory transmitters. Glycine administered by iontophoretic techniques was consistently found to diminish the firing and excitability of both spinal motor neurons and interneurons. This is interesting in itself since glycine is quite ineffective as an inhibitor of cortical neurons. In addition, the hyperpolarization and the changes in membrane permeability produced by glycine seem to be quite similar to those produced by the spinal inhibitory transmitter. Alteration in $K^+$ or $Cl^-$ ion concentrations affect the inhibitory postsynaptic potentials and the glycine-induced potentials in the same fashion. Strychnine, a compound which has been shown to reduce spinal postsynaptic inhibition, also blocks the effects of glycine on spinal motor neurons. It was originally reported that strychnine reversibly blocks the action of the natural inhibitory synaptic transmitter(s), as well as glycine and β-alanine, but does not have any effect on the hyperpolarizing action of GABA in cats anesthetized with pentobarbital. However, similar experiments on decerebrated unanesthetized cats have indicated that the qualitative dichotomy between glycine and β-alanine and

GABA originally reported does not usually hold. Instead, only a quantitative difference in the interaction of strychnine and the amino acids above is reported. In all these experiments, strychnine more potently antagonized glycine than GABA. However, GABA also inhibits these spinal neurons and is present endogenously, and in the course of distinguishing between the relative merits of GABA and glycine as inhibitory transmitter candidates in the spinal cord it was of interest to see if a loss of function of inhibitory interneurons would be accompanied by a change in one or both of these compounds. Anoxia of the lumbosacral cord produced by clamping the thoracic aorta seems to destroy the interneurons preferentially, while leaving 80 per cent or more of the motoneurons intact. Thus, the presynaptic cells responsible for inhibition (and other functions) are lost and therefore the concentration of transmitter associated with these cells would be expected to be decreased. When the effect of anoxia on GABA and glycine content of the cat spinal cord was analyzed, glycine was the only potential inhibitory amino acid markedly decreased. Thus the distribution of glycine in the spinal cord of the cat appears to be related to the inhibitory interneurons. Some preliminary results with perfused toad spinal cord have indicated that glycine release appears to occur during stimulation of the dorsal roots. However, the release of glycine from interneurons in the cord has not yet been demonstrated. In summary, glycine thus satisfies many of the criteria sufficiently to warrant its consideration as a possible inhibitory transmitter in the cat spinal cord.

    a. it occurs in the cat spinal cord associated with interneurons;

    b. when administered iontophoretically it hyperpolarizes motoneurons to the same equilibrium potential as postsynaptic inhibition;

    c. the permeability changes of the postsynaptic membrane induced by glycine appear to be similar to those associated with postsynaptic inhibition;

    d. strychnine, a drug which blocks the action of glycine, also blocks postsynaptic inhibition.

e. stimulation of dorsal roots causes release of glycine from perfused spinal cord.

The mechanisms by which the action of iontophoretically applied glycine or that of the putative spinal inhibitory transmitters are terminated is not known at this time. Recently, it has been demonstrated that there is an active and efficient sodium-dependent uptake mechanism for glycine in rat spinal cord and that labeled glycine taken up into slices can be released by electrical or potassium stimulation. However, whether or not this uptake mechanism is the physiological mechanism by which the action of administered or released glycine is terminated remains to be determined. Also, to date very little appears to be known with regard to the release of glycine from the spinal cord. Again, as with GABA the efficient uptake process may explain why it is difficult to detect glycine release from the central nervous system. The main problem (as with GABA, glutamate, etc.) is that there is no distinct neuronal pathway which may be isolated and stimulated; thus all the induced activity is very generalized, making the significance of any demonstrable release (metabolite or excess transmitter) very difficult to interpret.

To summarize then, probably the most critical missing piece of evidence to establish an even more complete identification of the inhibitory role of glycine in the spinal cord is the demonstration that glycine is the main substance contained in the terminals of the interneurons that synapse on the motoneurons and that it is glycine which is released from these terminals when direct inhibition is produced. Some partial support for the localization of glycine has been provided by autoradiographic localization of glycine uptake sites as visualized by electron microscopy. However, demonstration of discretely evoked release of glycine from spinal cord interneurons has been more difficult to obtain.

GLUTAMIC ACID

It has been recognized for many years that certain amino acids such as glutamate and aspartate occur in uniquely high concentrations in the brain and that they can exert very powerful stimulatory effects on neuronal activity. Thus, if any amino acid is involved in regulation of nerve cell activity, as an excitatory transmitter or otherwise, it seems unnecessary, at least at present, to look beyond these two candidates.

The excitatory potency of glutamate was first demonstrated on crustacean muscle and later by direct topical application to mammalian brain. However, except for the invertebrate model where glutamate is thought to be an excitatory neuromuscular transmitter, its status as a neurotransmitter in mammalian brain has not been significantly advanced. This is probably in part explainable by the fact that glutamate (and also aspartate) is a compound which is involved in intermediary metabolism in neural tissue and thus it has been extremely difficult to dissociate the role this amino acid plays in neuronal metabolism from its possible role as a transmitter substance. The presence of these amino acids is not restricted to a particular type of neuron as is acetylcholine and norepinephrine. Thus even if neuronal systems do exist in the CNS which utilize glutamate or aspartate as transmitter substances it seems quite unlikely that it will be possible to map out these systems by following the presence of glutamate or aspartate or their synthesizing enzymes.

The status of these substances as neurotransmitters has suffered through many cycles of acceptability and nonacceptability in the past decade. Even at the present time we still cannot say conclusively whether these substances are in fact transmitters in the central nervous system of mammals or, for that matter, even in invertebrates. The case for glutamate as a transmitter in the mammalian central nervous system is considerably weaker than that for acetylcholine, catecholamines, 5-HT, GABA, and glycine. In the vertebrate central nervous system, iontophoretic application of both glutamate and aspartate to nerve cells does produce depolarization and an increase in firing rate. In this connection, as was mentioned above, both GABA and L-glutamate are released from the cerebral cortex of the cat at a rate which appears to be dependent upon its state of CNS activation—more GABA and less L-glutamic acid being released under conditions associated with "sleep-like" EEG patterns, with the reverse situation occurring under arousal conditions. This differential release does not appear to result from alterations in cortical blood flow, since the release of other amino acids such as L-glutamine and L-aspartic acid does not vary similarly with different conditions. However, at this time it was not demonstrated that the origin of these amino acids was in fact from neurons or, for that matter, even from brain cells. The possibility could not be ruled out that these amino acids were derived from blood or cerebrospinal fluid. Although these experiments can be taken as supportive evidence for a role of these agents as transmitters, they by no means establish this role.

Some disturbing facts are that glutamate, aspartate, and synthetic derivatives of these dicarboxylic acids result in almost universal activation of unit discharge, and they appear to be almost ubiquitous in the nervous system without the expected asymmetric distribution. It has also been reported that glutamate does not bring the cell membrane potential to the same level as the natural excitatory transmitter. In addition, both the D and L isomers are active, although in the case of glutamate the D isomer is often reported to be somewhat less active. These findings have led many investigators to suggest that the response to amino acids represents a nonspecific receptivity of the neuron to these agents and is therefore not indicative of a transmitter function. However, the possibility still exists that glutamate may serve as a final excitatory agent in the chemical events involved in synaptic transmission.

Recently it has been observed that 1-hydroxy-3-aminopyrrolid-2-one (or compound HA-966) selectively antagonizes neuronal excitation evoked by the electrophoretic application of acidic amino acids. This agent might prove useful in evaluating the suspected transmitter role of glutamate or aspartate at a given synapse.

SELECTED REFERENCES

Aprison, M. H., R. A. Davidoff, and R. Werman (1970). Glycine: its metabolic and possible transmitter roles in nervous tissue. In *Handbook of Neurochemistry* (A. Lajtha, ed.). Vol. 3. Plenum, New York.

Baxter, C. F. (1970). The nature of γ-aminobutyric acid. In *Handbook of Neurochemistry* (A. Lajtha, ed.). Vol. 3. Plenum, New York.

Bloom, F. E. (1972). Amino acids and polypeptides in neuronal function. *Neurosciences Research Program Bulletin*, Vol. 10, 122.

Curtis, D. R. and J. M. Crawford (1969). Central synaptic transmission microelectropheretic studies. *Ann. Rev. Pharmacol. 9*, 209.

De Feudis, F. V., J. M. R. Delgado, and R. H. Roth (1970). Content, synthesis and collectability of amino acids in various structures of brain of Rhesus monkeys. *Brain Res. 18*, 15.

Euler, C. von, S. Skoglund, and U. Söderberg, eds. (1968). *Structure and Function of Inhibitory Neuronal Mechanisms.* Pergamon, New York.

Fahn, S., and L. J. Coté (1968). Regional distribution of γ-aminobutyric acid (GABA) in brain of the Rhesus monkey. *J. Neurochem. 15*, 209.

Iversen, L. L. (1972). The uptake, storage, release, and metabolism of GABA in inhibitory nerves. In *Perspectives in Neuropharmacology* (S. H. Snyder, ed.), p. 75, Oxford University Press, New York.

Johnson, J. L. (1972). Glutamic acid as a synaptic transmitter in the nervous system: a review. *Brain Res. 37*, 1.

Kravitz, E. A. (1967). Acetylcholine, γ-aminobutyric acid and glutamic acid: physiological and chemical studies related to their roles as neurotransmitter agents. In *The Neurosciences*. (G. D. Quarton, T. Melnechuk, and F. O. Schmitt, eds.), p. 433, Rockefeller University Press, New York.

Otsuka, M. (1973). Gamma aminobutyric acid and some other

transmitter candidates in the nervous system. *Proc. Int. Cong. Pharmacol. 4,* 186.

Roberts, E., C. F. Baxter, A. Van Harrefeld, C. A. G. Wiersma, W. R. Adey, and K. F. Kollam (1960). *Inhibition in the Nervous System and Gamma-aminobutyric Acid,* Pergamon, New York.

Roberts, E., and K. Kuriyama (1968). Biochemical-physiological correlations in studies of the γ-aminobutyric acid system. *Brain Res. 8,* 1.

Werman, R. (1972). Amino acids as central neurotransmitters. In *Neurotransmitters.* Res. Publ. A.R.N.M.D., Vol. 50, 147.

# 9 | Cyclic AMP, Prostaglandins, Substance P, and Histamine

## Adenosine 3',5'-Monophosphate (Cyclic AMP)

Primarily through the work of Sutherland and his associates, many hormonal actions are now known to be mediated by cyclic AMP. Epinephrine-stimulated glycogenolysis in skeletal muscle, the secretion of insulin, lipolysis in fat cells and the release of thyroid stimulating hormone, all appear to be under the control of this cyclic nucleotide. Until recently, evidence for a function of cyclic AMP in nervous tissue was only suggestive—brain contains the highest activity of any tissue of adenylate cyclase, the enzyme that catalyzes the synthesis of cyclic AMP from ATP, and of the phosphodiesterase that cleaves the cyclic nucleotide to AMP. In the past few years, however, a specific role of cyclic AMP in synaptic function has been elucidated.

By electrophysiological and cytochemical methods the inhibitory $\beta$-adrenergic receptors of cerebellar Purkinje cells have been studied with respect to the possibility that central $\beta$-receptors mediate their effects by activation of adenylate cyclase. Briefly, these experiments indicate that norepinephrine slows the mean rate of discharge of Purkinje cells by interaction with a beta receptor and that this slowing is produced by a prolongation of pauses between bursts of single spikes without effect on climbing fiber responses. Intracellular recordings revealed that norepinephrine hyperpolarizes the membrane of Purkinje cells and that this hyperpolarization is generally accompanied by increased membrane resistance (but never by increased membrane conductance (see Chapter 2)). The actions of norepinephrine on the Purkinje cell are blocked by iontophoretic application of prostaglandins of the E series and by nicotinate. All of these results suggest that the $\beta$-adrenergic receptor on Purkinje neurons is similar to the $\beta$-receptor of adipocytes. The effects of norepinephrine on discharge rate and membrane parameters are precisely emulated by iontophoretic application of cyclic AMP, and the effects of both the applied cyclic AMP and of norepinephrine are potentiated by any of several phosphodiesterase inhibitors. On the basis of these data, it has been proposed that the synaptic action of norepinephrine is mediated by an interaction via the adenylate cyclase of the Purkinje cells in the cerebellar cortex, which was known from neurochemical experiments *in vitro* to be highly responsive to norepinephrine. Since it has now been established that the cerebellar norepinephrine fibers arise from the nucleus locus coeruleus, this proposal could be tested further by activating and analyzing the effects of the pathway on Purkinje cell membrane properties. These experiments disclosed that stimulation of the pathway inhibited Purkinje cell discharge, especially single spike bursts, that the inhibitory effects of stimulating locus coeruleus required active synthesis of norepinephrine, and that no effects on cerebellar neuronal discharge were observed when the area of the locus was stimulated in animals pretreated with 6-hydroxydopamine (to eliminate the adrenergic projection to the cerebellum). By intracellular recording in cerebellum during stimulation of the locus coeruleus, Purkinje cells were found to be hyperpolarized and this hyperpolarization was again accompanied by a definitive increase in the resistance of the membrane. Similar effects of norepinephrine have also been observed in spinal motoneurons. Activation of the locus coeruleus inhibits spontaneous Purkinje discharge, and this effect—like that of norepinephrine—can be potentiated by local cerebellar iontophoresis of phosphodiesterase inhibitors onto the Purkinje cell and can be blocked by local iontophoretic administration of prostaglandins of the E series. All these results support the concept that this adrenergic projection could be operating by

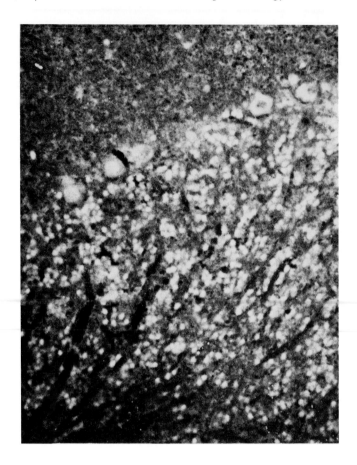

FIGURE 9-1. Immunocytochemical localization of cyclic AMP in neurons of the rat cerebellar cortex. Only two types of neurons exhibit staining after topical application of norepinephrine or electrical stimulation of the locus coeruleus: the large (20-30 μ) Purkinje neurons, which show positive staining in both cytoplasm and nucleus; and the granule cells (10μ), which show staining only in the nucleus. Under control conditions, granule cell staining patterns are the same, while only a few minimally reactive Purkinje cells exhibit staining. (Bloom *et al.*, 1973.)

production of a trans-synaptic elevation of cyclic AMP in Purkinje cells.

The proposed cyclic AMP mediation has now been documented by use of an immunocytochemical method with tissue sections. Using this method, topical application of norepinephrine or electrical activation of the locus coeruleus will elevate the number of Purkinje cells showing positive immunocytological staining for cyclic AMP from resting frequencies of 5 to 15 per cent to levels greater than 75 per cent (see Fig. 9.1).

A generally similar set of observations were made by Greengard and his coworkers on the dopaminergic intraganglionic synapses in rabbit sympathetic ganglia. In these ganglia, orthodromic stimuli will activate adenylate cyclase synaptically via a presumed muscarinic site on dopaminergic cells. In biochemical experiments, the adenylate cyclase of the ganglia is most responsive to dopamine, which is found mainly within small intensely fluorescent ganglionic interneurons. Application of dopamine to whole ganglia *in vitro* increases the cyclic AMP content and produces membrane hyperpolarization, as does cyclic AMP. The dopamine effects are enhanced by theophylline and blocked by prostaglandin $E_1$.

Let us now consider other consequences which may arise from these cyclic nucleotide mediated synapses. Based on the findings of E. Krebs and his colleagues on the phosphorylase system in muscle, Greengard has proposed that a general scheme for the post-synaptic response in such systems is the activation of protein kinases by cyclic AMP. Thus, a neurotransmitter such as norepinephrine or dopamine can be released from synapses to initiate a cascade of effects by which the synaptic actions are amplified (see Fig. 9-2). The neurotransmitter activates the cyclase to increase the rate of formation of the cyclic nucleotide, and the cyclic nucleotide can activate the protein kinases. Two related concepts follow directly from this line of thought. Phosphorylation of a synaptic membrane protein might be expected to alter membrane permeability; thus, it is possible that the increased membrane polarization and the decreased membrane permeability generated by the activation of adenylate cyclase are only epiphenomena of

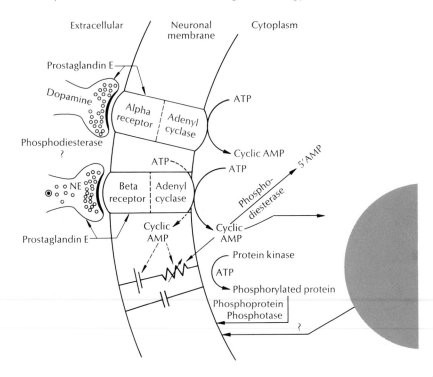

the process by which cyclic AMP concentration is increased. Furthermore, the electrical effects of these synapses may be less important for their short-term interactions (i.e. with other synaptic potentials being generated simultaneously) than for longer term trophic effects on the properties of the postsynaptic cell. For example, cyclic AMP can affect the molecular synthesis of RNA and of proteins in other cell systems, apart from its more general role in carbohydrate metabolism.

This concept warrants generalization from cyclic AMP to cyclic nucleotides because of the likelihood that future research will reveal equally specific synaptic controls for control of cyclic guanosine monophosphate (cyclic GMP). The cellular roles which may be mediated by transmitters that accelerate cyclic GMP synthesis are only beginning to be studied, but preliminary evidence suggests an interaction between cyclic GMP and ACh.

FIGURE 9-2. A schematic representation of the possible interactions of cyclic AMP mediated synaptic receptor mechanisms and their consequent actions on neuronal metabolism. A mythical neuron is illustrated receiving a synaptic contact from a dopamine-containing terminal and from a norepinephrine-containing terminal. Both have been described on separate cell types, but never on the same cell. In the schema, both catecholamines are able to activate adenylate cyclase, the dopamine via an alpha receptor, and norepinephrine via a beta receptor. The cyclic AMP which is formed and which survives phosphodiesterase catabolism can go on to activate cyclic AMP dependent protein kinases. Two such kinase actions are illustrated: one action of the protein kinase could be to phosphorylate proteins in the synaptic membrane, which could then alter the resistive and capacitative properties of the membrane (the symbols for which are drawn across the membrane at lower left); a second action of protein kinase within neurons could also be to phosphorylate nuclear histones, thereby changing the extent to which genetic properties are being expressed in the current metabolic properties of the cell. The latter mechanism might also be capable of altering electrical or pharmacological properties of the cell membrane through the classical DNA-RNA-protein route over a longer time course of action. Prostaglandins of the E series act similarly on the adenylate cyclase sensitivity of the only two systems known to exhibit these properties, namely, the cerebellar Purkinje neurons' sensitivity to norepinephrine and the sympathetic ganglion neurons' sensitivity to dopamine. For further details and references, see text.

It is far from clear at present whether cells can use both types of cyclic nucleotides to mediate contrasting regulations of individual cellular functions or whether specific nucleotides act within restricted cell populations to serve selective messenger roles.

To summarize, then, a rather complex sequence of reactions for which evidence is slowly accumulating, the following events are postulated to occur. Neuronal stimulation causes release of a transmitter which then impinges on the postsynaptic cell. Here the transmitter activates adenylate cyclase to increase the rate of production of the cyclic nucleotide. This nucleotide then activates a protein kinase to phosphorylate, via ATP, some protein substrate. The phosphorylated membrane protein permits a change in ion permeability with a resulting depolarization or hyperpolarization, depending on the equilibrium potential in the cell of the various ions.

Specificity in this system is thought to be conferred both by the protein kinase and the protein substrate that is phosphorylated. The activity of the system is terminated both by phosphodiesterase, which cleaves the cyclic nucleotide, and a phosphoprotein phosphatase that dephosphorylates the phosphorylated protein to its native form. It is still not clear how many substrate proteins, protein kinases, phosphodiesterases, or phosphoprotein phosphatases exist.

To summarize further, at present we know of five proteins that are involved in the cyclic nucleotide sequence described above. These are adenylate cyclase, phosphodiesterase, substrate protein, protein kinase, and phosphoprotein phosphatase. According to the scheme, all five proteins should be localized postsynaptically. Evidence of this postsynaptic localization remains to be obtained.

PROSTAGLANDINS

In 1935 von Euler discovered a substance in human seminal plasma and sheep vesicular glands which he thought was secreted by the prostate gland. This substance, for which he coined the name "prostaglandin," appeared to be an active acidic lipid with smooth muscle stimulatory and depressant activity. Since the chemical structure of this class of substances was not elucidated until almost thirty years later, the term "prostaglandin"—although a misnomer—had sufficient time to become firmly ingrained in the literature. In fact, this term is still used today as a generic name for the whole class of chemical compounds occurring naturally in a variety of tissues that are related derivatives of prostanoic acid. Thus, the term "prostaglandin" is now generically applied to designate one of sixteen or more chemically distinct natural constituents extractable from various mammalian tissues. There are two major series of prostaglandins, the E series (those which were originally found to extract into ether) in which the five-membered ring has one hydroxyl and one keto group and the F series (those which were extracted by fosphate [Sw.] buffer) in which the substituents are both hydroxyls (Fig. 9-3). Although many different biological roles have been ascribed to this class of compounds, we will limit our discussion here to their postulated roles in innervated tissues and in the brain.

Prostaglandins seem clearly able to alter the physiology of the sympathetic nervous system, probably having dual action on the release of transmitter from adrenergic terminals and the responsiveness of the postsynaptic cell to norepinephrine. Available data are very difficult to generalize since the actions observed are

FIGURE 9-3. Structure of prostaglandins.

highly dependent on the state of the test system, the rate of its activation, and the nature of the postsynaptic cell type. Nevertheless, it seems clear that $PGE_1$ and $PGE_2$ can inhibit the effects of the sympathetic nervous system in rabbit and guinea pig heart, in cat and dog spleen, and in the vas deferens of several species. Hedqvist has proposed that these actions relate to decreased transmitter release per impulse. The effects can be observed with extremely small concentrations of prostaglandins, on the order of $10^{-10}M$ or less. The release of prostaglandins from the stomach can be induced by vagal or transmural stimulation; however, it has been claimed that this release is from muscle cells and not from nerve terminals since stomach strips stored in the cold for three days to allow degeneration of nerve fibers still release prostaglandins.

It is now quite well established that the central nervous system contains a number of different prostaglandins. These substances are also normal constituents of cerebrospinal fluid. Generally, the mammalian CNS contains predominantly the PGF series, with small amounts of a PGE in some cases. The concentration of prostaglandins found in the mammalian central nervous system is in the range of 100-200 ng/gm. Reports also indicate that brain has the enzymatic capacity for the synthesis of some prostaglandins. The current view is that PGE's are stored minimally and that most of the PGE released from the brain derives from a newly synthesized pool. The distribution of these substances in the central nervous system appears to be fairly uniform and certainly does not vary widely enough to suggest that prostaglandins may be exclusively associated with specific pathways in the brain, as are the many other putative transmitters considered in previous chapters.

Many prostaglandins are also released from superfused cat cerebral or cerebellar cortex. The release from the somatosensory cortex can be greatly increased by direct or contralateral stimulation of the cortex. If the corpus callosum is sectioned, the release is limited to the stimulated side. Release from the cortex can also be increased by afferent nerve stimulation. The release induced in the contralateral cortex by stimulation of the radial nerve is frequency dependent, being maximal at 0.25-1/sec and minimal at 30-100/sec. Prostaglandin release has also been demonstrated in ventricular perfusates. Again, although much research has been devoted to the release of prostaglandins from central sites, it has not been possible to determine the release of prostaglandins from localized areas of the central nervous system in response to stimulation of well-defined anatomical pathways.

A number of pharmacological stimulants can also evoke the release of prostaglandins from the central nervous system. The most notable are picrotoxin, pentylenetetrazole, and strychnine. The release of prostaglandins E and F from the cat cerebellar cortex is also increased after electrical stimulation of the reticular formation and this increased release can be blocked if the animal is pretreated with chlorpromazine.

Studies on rat brain cortical homogenates indicate that PGE may be associated to some extent with the synaptosome fraction, although not with synaptic vesicles. The biosynthetic enzymes appear, however, to be localized to the "microsomal" fraction.

None of the above evidence indicates that prostaglandins act as typical CNS neurotransmitters. Early neuropharmacological analyses of the actions of the prostaglandins coupled the injections of extremely large doses of the lipids into the ventricular system of the brain with rather gross behavioral observations. Animals in such experiments, perhaps not surprisingly, showed severe behavioral depression. More discrete tests were possible when the prostaglandins were administered by iontophoresis, but the results of these initial tests—like many of the results reported with iontophoresis in general—were inconclusive: some unidentified brain stem cells were speeded, some were slowed, most did not respond at all, and many of those that did exhibited tachyphylaxis. Clearly, a new line of investigation was needed.

A key to the functional role of prostaglandins in many other organs of the body is their interaction with adenylate cyclase. Depending on the tissue, prostaglandins can either increase or decrease cyclic AMP synthesis or degradation. In fact, with the exception of adipose tissue and the toad bladder, all other tissues tend to show increased cyclic AMP levels after exposure to prostaglandins. Since prostaglandins are a natural constituent of the cerebellum, and since there is a noradrenergic inhibitory pathway to cerebellar Purkinje cells which is mediated by cyclic AMP, this test system offered an opportunity to explore the actions of prostaglandins. It was found that iontophoretic administration of $PGE_1$ or $PGE_2$—but no other PG—would block the response of Purkinje cells to norepinephrine and to the effects of activation of the noradrenergic pathway but did not affect the response of Purkinje cells to other inhibitory pathways or to other inhibitory substances, including the actions of cyclic AMP itself. These results fit best with the view that endogenous cerebellar PG's act as do those of the adipocyte: their release from cells receiving adrenergic innervation blocks the norepinephrine-sensitive adenylate cyclase and prevents the hormonally induced rise in intracellular cyclic AMP. Such a negative feedback synaptic arrangement would offer the possibility of local synaptic modulations. For such studies to continue, a whole new range of specific drugs is needed to attempt probing of the PG receptor and the site of PG synthesis and release. The metabolism of the prostaglandins and sites of actions of inhibitors are shown in Fig. 9-4.

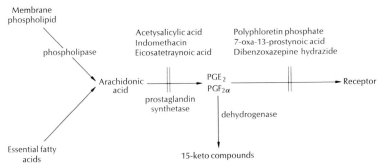

FIGURE 9-4. Prostaglandin metabolism, inhibitors, and sites of action. Phospholipase activity, assumed to be the rate-limiting step in the synthesis of the prostaglandins, is activated by inflammatory and mechanical stimuli and by hormones. (Modified after Sears et al. (1973).)

## SUBSTANCE P

In 1931 von Euler and Gaddum were assaying ACh in extracts from brain and intestine when they detected the presence of another pharmacologically active substance, later named substance P because it was isolated in the form of a powder. This name has turned out to be much more appropriate than the authors realized some 40 years ago since it is now known that substance P is in fact structurally a polypeptide. To date, however, its physiological function is still quite obscure. The only difference in the substance P of intestinal origin and that isolated from the central nervous system appears to be the greater lability of the brain preparation. Pharmacologically, this substance has both smooth muscle contractile activity and vasodilatory activity. In these pharmacological actions substance P is one of the most potent agents known, especially on a molar basis, since 2 to 3 ng injected into man will produce a marked effect on blood flow.

More recently, the properties of increasingly pure ($1-2 \times 10^5$ times the potency of the original preparation of Euler and Gaddum) preparations of substance P have been more fully investigated. Most of the purest preparations contain a basic polypeptide composed of the same 13 amino acids. The molecular weight of this peptide has been estimated to be about 1000. One of the greatest difficulties in preparing and purifying this material is that it becomes more and more unstable with each stage of purification.

Substance P is distributed almost exclusively in the digestive tract and the nervous system. All peripheral nerves and ganglia studied appear to contain this substance, and it is found in all the layers of the intestine. Euler observed that substance P is present in peripheral nerves in subcellular particles ("microsomes") from which it can be released by hypotonic solutions, acid, or heat treatment. However, no evidence is available to suggest whether or not substance P is stored in similar subcellular particles in brain. All determinations of the distribution of substance P in the central nervous system of cats, dogs, cattle, and humans have been made by bioassay. The more recent quantitative estimations have been made by means of the terminal ileum of the quinea pig. The assays are usually performed in the presence of atropine, a serotonin antagonist, and an antihistamine, in order to prevent the stimulatory effect on the gut of acetylcholine, 5-hydroxytryptamine, and histamine, any or all of which could occur in tissue extracts. These precautions do not necessarily exclude the possibility that materials other than substance P are acting on the ileum, but the presence of another polypeptide (bradykinin) can be excluded by using the hen's rectal caecum, which is either insensitive or relaxes in the presence of bradykinin. Despite the difficulty in accurately bioassaying this substance, there appears to be general agreement that it is widely distributed in nervous tissue, with a localized distribution in certain parts of the brain. In general, the concentration of substance P appears to decrease with increasing differentiation of the central nervous system. In human brain the substantia nigra contains the highest concentration, approximately 1000 units/gm. Next in order are the floor of the fourth ventricle and the inferior colliculus, followed by the midbrain, hypothalamus, caudate nucleus, and thalamus. With the exception of the spinal cord, white matter contains less substance P than gray matter. In the spinal cord there is an interesting discrepancy between dorsal and ventral roots. The dorsal roots contain about ten times as much substance P as the ventral roots.

This unequal distribution in various brain regions, together with the finding that brain contains an enzyme that inactivates substance P, has led some investigators to postulate a transmitter role for the substance. Over the many years following its discovery there have been numerous reports concerning the central nervous system effects produced by substance P. However, the highly purified preparation of Haefely and Hurlimann did not have any significant effect on the central nervous system, even when administered in high doses intravenously or intracerebrally, so it was concluded that the pharmacological effects reported originally were due largely to impurities in the preparation. The enzyme system responsible for the synthesis of substance P is unknown and therefore has not been localized. While there is no direct evidence that substance P is released during neuronal activation, retinal substance P increases in animals maintained in darkness and decreases after exposure to light, implying that the levels within this tissue may be controlled by impulse activity. Most bothersome has been the observation that substance P did not produce any effects on individual neurons. Only two positive bits of evidence favor a functional role for this substance: the report that the concentration of substance P decreases in degenerating neurons and the report that during Wallerian degeneration of sensory nerves the concentration of substance P in the proximal stump increases while that in the distal end falls.

Nonetheless, this area of research has been dramatically reactivated by the purification of substance P from the hypothalamus, by the sequencing of its amino acid structure, and by the subsequent synthesis of a polypeptide which exhibits isomolar activity with the natural compound. The polypeptide is also antigenic and the immune serum produced provides an extremely sensitive immunoassay system. Most recently, investigators have been able to retest the possible actions of substance P on neurons of the frog dorsal root ganglia, using synthetic substance P. The dorsal root ganglia are a natural test site because they contain far more of this compound than other nerve trunks that can be isolated. These studies showed that substance P in fact is extremely potent, causing significant depolarization of the cells at $1 \times 10^{-7}$M. The application of peptide purification methods to the central nervous system, particularly the hypothalamus, has revealed a multitude of biogenic peptides, and some may turn out to act on tissues other than the anterior pituitary.

## HISTAMINE

A quick glance at this book reveals that the major emphasis on the biogenic amines in the nervous system has been devoted to norepinephrine, dopamine, and 5-hydroxytryptamine rather than histamine. This is due, in part, to the great bulk of contradictory evidence on histamine, especially regarding its possible relation to mental disease. Of course, some of the more recent conflicts may be resolved in view of the fact that the spectrophotometric assay so often used to measure brain histamine has been found to be completely unreliable since it measures other normal constituents of brain such as spermidine and histidine. Thus much of the research concerned with histamine in the central nervous system will have to be repeated with new methodology before it can be properly evaluated. Recently, a new sensitive radiometric method has been developed with which it is possible to measure less than 10 picograms of tissue histamine. With this method the regional distribution of histamine in monkey brain has been studied in great detail. In confirmation of earlier studies the highest concentration of histamine was found in certain nuclei of the hypothalamus.

The actual physiological significance of brain histamine however still remains obscure, even though its presence in nervous tissue has been recognized for many years. Some peripheral nerves such as the sympathetic postganglionic fibers are also particularly rich in histamine. Its release from certain peripheral nerves implies a role for histamine as a transmitter substance, but the fact that the histamine content of sensory nerves usually rises progressively after degeneration, rather than being lost from the nerve like other putative transmitter substances, contradicts this implication.

In the hope of obtaining a better insight into the neuronal function of histamine, many studies have been carried out on the effect of exogenous histamine on transmission in the superior cervical ganglion of the cat. It is now known that small doses (as little as $0.1$ $\mu$g) of histamine facilitate submaximal ganglionic transmission and potentiate the response of the ganglion to ACh, nicotine, carbachol, choline, and other substances. Histamine in higher doses (greater than $1$ $\mu$g) directly stimulates the nonperfused ganglion, while the perfused ganglion is less sensitive to histamine. This effect is opposed by cocaine, morphine, and various depolarizing ganglionic blocking agents. Even larger amounts of histamine ($\sim$ $150$ $\mu$g) block transmission of supramaximal preganglionic impulses through the superior cervical ganglion. These findings on the superior cervical ganglia are thus consistent with the hypothesis that histamine may function in the nervous system in a "neuromodulatory role." It is interesting that small amounts of histamine (1-4 $\mu$g) inhibit transcallosally evoked potentials in the cat cortex, suggesting that histamine may function as a synaptic inhibitor. Many workers in this field question the validity and significance of this finding since almost every agent tried in this system seems to produce inhibition. Applied iontophoretically to neurons in the lateral geniculate and spinal cord, histamine has little or no activity. On cortical neurons, however, histamine has some inhibitory effects although it is much less potent than $\gamma$-aminobutyric acid.

The large quantities of histamine (up to 100 $\mu$g/gm, seven times that of the adrenergic transmitter) in postganglionic sympathetic fibers also suggests that it may participate in some way in the regulation of peripheral nervous activity. However, little evidence for the existence of histaminergic nerves has been forthcoming over the years. In fact, the histamine in these nerves has often been ascribed to mast cells and has been considered to be unrelated to axons. Yet the histamine found in mast cell granules sediments with material denser than mitochondria, while the particulate histamine in splenic nerve sediments with material of less density than mitochondria. In addition, it has been observed that perfusion of the sciatic nerve with compound 48/80, a substance which releases mast cell histamine, only released about 25 per cent of the nerve histamine. *In vivo* treatment of dogs with either 48/80 or reserpine does not deplete postganglionic sympathetic nerves of histamine. These experiments support the contention that the histamine in these nerves is not associated with mast cells.

Mast cells are absent from the central nervous system, except for restricted areas, and the histamine there must reside in some other cellular component. The subcellular distribution of brain histamine is consistent with the hypothesis that it is contained in nerve endings. It is also of interest that the general pattern of distribution of histamine in the brain is much like that of the other biogenic amines such as norepinephrine and 5-hydroxytrypta-mine. The concentration is high in the hypothalamus (in fact there is twice as much histamine as 5-hydroxytryptamine here), intermediate in the midbrain, and lowest in the cortex and white matter. It is surprising that many investigators refer to the 0.1-0.5 $\mu$g/gm of histamine found by Crossland and Garven as very low and therefore of doubtful significance. Yet it is commonly stated that the hypothalamus contains a high concentration of 5-hydroxy-tryptamine, although its actual content is often no more than about 0.5 $\mu$g/gm.

Recent experiments have shown that cat brain can form his-tamine from histidine and can convert histamine to methyl histamine and methylimidazole acetic acid (Fig. 9-5). The meth-ylating enzyme imidazole-$N$-methyltransferase has been isolated from cat brain. For many years it was believed that the enzyme responsible for the formation of histamine from histidine was the nonspecific aromatic-L-amino acid decarboxylase. The properties of this enzyme have been described in some detail in Chapter 5. However, recent experiments have uncovered a rather specific histidine decarboxylase existing in various mammalian tissues. Whether or not this specific enzyme is the enzyme responsible for the formation of histamine in neuronal tissue has yet to be conclusively demonstrated. A prototype for the specific histidine decarboxylase has been partially purified from fetal rat tissue. This enzyme is inhibited by $\alpha$-methylhistamine but not to any extent by $\alpha$-methyl DOPA, an inhibitor of aromatic amino acid decarboxylase. In this regard it is of interest that labeled histamine is formed from intraventricularly administered [3]H-histidine. This formation of labeled histamine can be effectively inhibited with $\alpha$-hydrazine-histidine but not with $\alpha$-methyl DOPA.

Histamine metabolism in the brain is influenced by drugs known to be centrally active. Reserpine, for example, reduces the concentration of histamine in the hypothalamus and thalamus just as it reduces the concentration of other amines there, although not to the same extent. Tremorine also decreases brain histamine. Chlorpromazine, which partially inhibits $N$-methyltransferase, in-

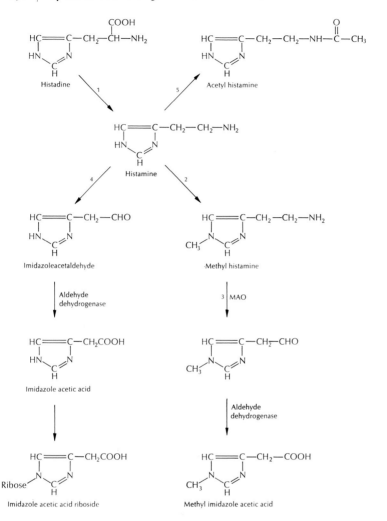

FIGURE 9-5. Metabolism of histamine. (1) Histidine decarboxylase. (2) Histamine methyl transferase. The major pathway for inactivation in most mammalian species. (3) Monoamine oxidase. (4) Histaminase. (5) Minor pathway of histamine catabolism.

creases the histamine concentration. However, these findings give little insight into the function of histamine in the central nervous system. Unlike other bioactive amines, histamine is not taken up against a concentration gradient by brain slices or synaptosomes.

Recently Davies and Meade have been successful in making antibodies to histamine. This offers the distinct possibility of employing immunohistochemical methods to visualize this substance in nervous tissue. Of course, it is extremely tempting to speculate that in the future it will be possible to make antibodies to other putative transmitter substances which would greatly expand our knowledge of the chemical organization of the brain.

SELECTED REFERENCES

*Cyclic AMP*

Greengard, P., D. A. McAfee, and J. W. Kebabian (1972). On the mechanism of action of cyclic AMP and its role in synaptic transmission. *Adv. in Cyclic Nucleotide Res.*, Vol. 1, p. 337. Raven Press, New York.

Hoffer, B. J., G. R. Siggins, A. P. Oliver, and F. E. Bloom (1973). Activation of the pathway from locus coeruleus to rat cerebellar Purkinje neurons: pharmacological evidence for noradrenergic central inhibition. *J. Pharm. Exp. Therap. 184,* 553.

Sutherland, E. (1972). Studies on the mechanism of hormone action. *Science 177,* 401.

*Prostaglandins*

Euler, U. S. von, and R. Eliasson (1967). *Prostaglandins.* Academic Press, New York.

Hinman, J. W. (1972). *Prostaglandins. Ann. Rev. Biochemistry 41,* 161.

Hoffer, B. J., G. R. Siggins, A. P. Oliver, and F. E. Bloom (1972). Cyclic AMP mediates adrenergic synapses to cerebellar Purkinje cells. *Adv. Cyclic Nucleotide Res. 1,* 411.

Sears, M. L., A. H. Neufeld, and L. M. Jampol (1973). Prostaglandins. *Invest. Opth. 12,* 161.

*Substance P*

Chang, M. M., and S. E. Leeman (1970). Isolation of a sialogogic peptide from bovine hypothalamus tissue and its characterization as substance P. *J. Biol. Chem. 245,* 4784.

Haefely, W., and A. Hurlimann (1962). Substance P, a highly active naturally occurring polypeptide. *Experientia 18*, 297.

Lembeck, F., and E. A. Zeller (1962). Substance P: a polypeptide of possible physiological significance, especially within the nervous system. *Int. Rev. Neurobiology 4*, 159.

## Histamine

Davies, T. R. A., and K. M. Meade (1970). Biologically active antibodies to histamine. *Nature 226*, 360.

Green, J. P. (1970). Histamine: in central mechanisms in the nervous system. In *Handbook of Neurochemistry* (A. Lajtha, ed.) Vol. 4, p. 221. Plenum, New York.

Rocha, E., and M. Siva (1966). Histamine: its chemistry, metabolism and physiological and pharmacological actions. *Handbuch der experimentellen Pharmakologie 18*, 1.

Snyder, S. H., and K. M. Taylor (1972). Histamine in the brain: a neurotransmitter? In *Perspectives in Neuropharmacology* (S. H. Snyder, ed.), p. 43. Oxford University Press, New York.

# 10 | Cellular Mechanisms in Memory and Learning

AT THE PRESENT time no one has shown unequivocally a causal relation between a change in cell structure or function and learning. In reality this sentence is all that is necessary to discuss this topic. Nevertheless we feel compelled to examine the theories and the experimental findings in this field for two reasons. First, this area comes under the domain of neuropharmacology since drugs have been used both directly to stimulate learning and indirectly as tools to explore molecular mechanisms which may be involved. Second, there is a great deal of appeal and excitement attached to this topic; thus we feel an obligation to prevent the impressionable and the romantically inclined from being seduced into this glamorous field before they know the pitfalls.

Before proceeding further it is necessary to define some terms that are encountered. "Memory" may be defined as the storage and retrieval of sensory information. Many investigators refer to "short-term memory" which is likened to reverberatory circuits and which operationally may be ablated by coma, anesthesia, or electroconvulsive therapy. "Long-term memory" refers to the consolidation of information with long-term storage and has been suggested to involve protein synthesis. It is still not clear if there is a sequential progression of short-term into long-term memory or if two different mechanisms are concerned. By "learning" we mean the modification of behavior through experience. However, since this simple definition would not exclude phenomena such as synaptic facilitation, post-tetanic potentiation, sensory adaptation, or fatigue, some investigators prefer a more detailed definition. They define learning as "a modification of a stimulus-response complex which involves the afferent nervous system and which in whole animals results in a new favorable adaptation." It is obvious that memory and learning are related, but memory is only a part of learning since learning infers a change in performance due to a gain in our understanding.

There are two other terms we should consider. "Sensitization" refers to an augmentation of a response to the conditioned stimulus. This means that the system becomes more efficient in being able to perceive or transmit the sensory stimuli and evoke the appropriate motor response. The opposite of sensitization is "habituation" which implies a progressive decrease in response to a given sensory signal. That this suppression is not due to a general fatigue of an organism may be shown by changing the stimulus and noting a return of a full response.

## FORMULATING THEORIES ON MEMORY AND LEARNING

Theories on memory and learning existed long before the anatomy of the nervous system was known. However, once the neuron was recognized as the basic functional unit of the nervous system, Ramon y Cajal was among the first to postulate that the process of learning involves structural changes at synaptic contacts. He apparently based this view upon the fact that with maturation of the nerve cells the dendritic trees sprouted spines as a sign of their complex maturation. He recognized that the synaptic contact was the primary site of communication between nerve cells and seemed to be a logical point at which to alter the efficiency of the information passage. Furthermore, he believed that electrical activity of one cell would favor the development of connections to a second cell, and thus that the availability of sensory inputs activating certain parts of the system would favor the development of new connections to other portions of the system.

The essential feature of this "specific connection" view of learning is that the experienced input modified the output by making a change either in the efficiency of the existing connection or by making more or newer connections between specific nervous cells. The opposite view was taken by many American psychologists during the early part of the twentieth century. They held that specific pathways or pre-existing connections between nerve cells had little or nothing to do with the learning process, and emphasized instead changes in nerve cell activity related to the external environment of the cell: possibly the extracellular space, possibly the electrical gradients from one portion of the cortex across another. In general this "field" theory depended upon influences much larger than any single cell or single group of cells. While the comprehension of this "field" or "global" model of learning presents many difficulties, the greatest one perhaps is that it is nearly impossible to subject the theory to experimental testings. On the other hand, the cellular or connectionistic viewpoint of learning can be subjected to modern electrophysiological and morphological techniques.

## Morphological Experiments

If activity within a defined nerve-to-nerve connection is able to influence the subsequent transmission through that same connection, then one might expect to find morphological variations associated with use and disuse. Numerous experiments along this line of investigation have been attempted, but the results offer little in the way of concrete support. The failure may be due to the fact that over-use or under-use are often produced by highly nonphysiological techniques such as cutting muscles, cutting nerves, or prolonged electrical stimulation. Another negative aspect may be that the systems involved are not necessarily those at which plastic or dynamic structural properties exist. However, even within the central nervous system, in areas such as the visual cortex or lateral geniculate (a relay nucleus of the visual system), it has been nearly impossible to demonstrate long-term changes in either electrical conduction or morphological connections with variations in activity through the visual system. With the electron microscope it may be possible to use specific staining reactions to quantitate the number and size of specialized synaptic contacts and thus to obtain a more objective measurement than can be made with empirical silver staining techniques which are often hit or miss in their resolution of nerve cells.

The types of experiments which have been reported center upon the neuromuscular junction or on other forms of reinnervated peripheral junctions such as sympathetic ganglia or other muscle preparations. Here it can be shown that when the muscle is kept at rest, or when the nerve is cut and the transmission across the junction is reduced, the muscle develops increased receptiveness for the neurotransmitter, namely, acetylcholine. This would suggest that disuse affects the junction by making it more sensitive to transmission. This is the opposite of the more commonly expressed view that usage favors the efficiency of transmission whereas nonusage impairs it. In the central nervous system, these two opposing views have not been studied in clearcut experiments and no final answer can be given at present. When animals are deprived of their visual imput by closing both eyes at birth before the first perception of sensory stimuli, there are no changes in neurophysiological conduction of signals when both eyes are subsequently opened. However, more complex changes can be seen: if one eye is kept closed and the other allowed to develop normally, the normally occurring bilateral interaction between the eyes cannot be subsequently demonstrated. Such findings fail to discriminate between activity required for development and activity affecting efficiency of usage.

## Cellular Models for Learning Experiments

The experimental tasks required to determine the nature of the cellular processes underlying the changes which occur with learning constitute one of the most difficult problem areas in science. It is essential to uncover a neuronal system in which experience, in the form of electrical stimulation, chemical stimulation, or natural stimulation (such as light or sound) can be shown to induce permanent changes in the conduction of impulses and which would thus offer a cellular model for the learning mechanism. Such a model has not yet been described.

However, numerous experiments have been reported (see the review by Kandel and Spencer) in which scientists have attempted to break down the behavioral analogues of the learning procedure, as based on the conditioned stimulus, condition avoidance, or operant types of learning situations. These experiments have indicated clearly that prolonged types of physiological change can be induced by activity. All cells do not exhibit these changes, but only particular cells such as giant neurons in molluscan ganglia or pacemaker type cells in simpler systems. When the transmembrane potential level is analyzed during these experiments, the plastic or experimentally induced changes in activity do not appear to arise from changes induced in the postsynaptic cell, its transmembrane resistance or capacitance, or the spike generating system. Therefore, whatever the changes are, they appear to be either within the synapse or on the presynaptic side of the system involved in the conditioning or learning. The mechanisms which have been suggested involve hyperpolarization of the presynaptic terminals by activity in the conditioning system: this hyperpolarization results in an enhanced effect through the test circuit when it is effectively stimulated and could cause an increased response to the conditioning. The effects need not involve two different circuits since prolonged stimulation of a single monosynaptic pathway can also result in enhanced effects of that pathway simply due to post-tetanic hyperpolarization. Such effects can last for hours. In similar fashion, the suggestion has been made that habituation could result from depression in the test pathway due to prolonged activity in the conditioning pathways which could in turn arise from enhancement of inhibitory postsynaptic potentials.

The problem, however, in relation to mammalian learning, is that experiments on molluscan ganglia, or even headless insect ganglia, confirm only the possibility that prolonged, possibly permanent, changes in the relationship of transmission between one or more cells in the circuit can be demonstrated. They do not tell us that these types of plastic changes can exist in higher forms or

260 | The Biochemical Basis of Neuropharmacology

that they are the only possible mechanisms by which plastic change may occur. Therefore, we must hope that neuronal systems for studying the learning process in animals more closely related to the mammal can be uncovered and that their mechanisms can be studied with the same types of cellular techniques.

Until a system for such study evolves, it appears fruitless to attempt to analyze with the electron microscope the possible plastic changes occurring in the mammalian central nervous system. Although we can suggest numerous possible mechanisms for such plastic change (such as increased size of specialized synaptic contacts, increased size of dendritic spines, increased numbers of synaptic vesicles), none of these changes can be documented meaningfully until we are able to identify a neuronal circuit in which a defined physiological function has been altered by the factors of use, disuse, or some other equivalent of the learning experience situation. The numerous variables involved in the size, number, and density of synaptic contacts for any particular nerve cell of the mammalian central nervous system is as yet poorly defined, and until such variables can be eliminated and until a specific circuit can be studied by both physiology and fine structure, an electron microscopic study on the learning process would seem to be much like the proverbial hunt for a needle in a haystack, except that in this case the needle may not exist at all.

Ripples of excitement have recently run through this field of cellular psychobiology following the demonstration that certain tracts within the mammalian brain may in fact be capable of true structural plasticity over a long time period. Although it had been known for some time that a small amount of plasticity, in the form of local axonal sprouts could occur in transected nerves, especially in immature animals and throughout the life cycle of many forms of amphibia and lower vertebrates, the recently described occurrence of similar phenomena in mammals immediately suggests a new stalking ground in the search for structural changes which may accompany learning. It is perhaps not unexpected that the transmitter involved in the circuits which show the most prominent propensity for collateral sprouting over long distances is norepinephrine, for it is this transmitter for which we have the most sensitive microscopical methods of detection and analysis. Most recently it has been possible to show that the sprouted axon collaterals extended by central catecholamine neurons do establish functional connections, at least in the cerebellar cortex. Perhaps this line of experimentation will begin to illuminate underlying dynamic properties of some families of nerve cells, and show that some of these properties may also play a role in whatever changes occur in long-term memory establishment.

Concurrent with electrophysiological approaches to the study of memory and learning, a number of neuroscientists have attempted to uncover molecular mechanisms in behavior using drugs as tools. We will now consider this biochemical approach.

## Biochemical Experimentation on Learning and Memory

As Kandell and Spencer point out, biochemical investigations on cellular mechanisms involved in memory and learning can be classified into four approaches:

1. *Facilitation.* Numerous investigators have used a variety of drugs in an attempt to increase the rate of learning. Agents that have been used include strychnine, picrotoxin, magnesium pemoline, RNA, amphetamine, and $K^+$. Positive, negative, and inconclusive results have been obtained with this approach. Such a range is almost predictable in view of the enormous number of variables involved: the type of drug used, the route of administration, the dose, the type of task involved in learning, and the strain, sex, and age of organisms that are tested. To these complexities we must also add the time element in the experiment, that is, giving the drug before learning or after learning, testing immediately or later. Even if a positive result were obtained, the effect of the drug could still be completely nonspecific and bear no primary relationship to the learning process but only to the rate of processing of information, for example, by an arousal effect on the animal.

2. *Transfer.* This line of investigation involves the administra-

tion of brain extracts from trained animals to untrained ones (referred to as naïve). These naïve recipients are then compared with control animals to see if their ability to learn the task is facilitated. Planaria (flatworms) were among the first organisms to be used in these experiments since not only are they cannibalistic, but they can be bisected and each half will regenerate the lost half-torso complete with rudimentary nervous system. There are two major problems with these planaria experiments: first, an enormous number of unknown variables must exist, since it has been difficult for one laboratory to duplicate results from another; second, the more basic unresolved question, do planaria learn? The known variables that require rigid control are the species and the source of the worms, the kind of training they receive, the amount and type of food they are given, the kind of shock that is administered, the time of day the experiments are done, the amount of handling the worms receive, the condition of their trough (planaria leave slime trails), the ion concentration of the water, and the light sensitivity of the worms. In addition, in early experiments the bias of the investigator was not controlled.

Mice and rats have also been used in transfer experiments. Ungar injected mice with brain extracts from rats that were habituated to sound and stated that the mice lost their startle response to the same sound stimulus. It was also reported that these mice responded normally to air-puff whereas mice that were injected with brain extracts from rats habituated to air-puff had a decreased response to air-puff but not to sound. Other experiments involved Y-maze training in which the rats in order to escape a shock were trained to run into the lighted arm of the maze. Brain extracts from the trained rats were then injected i.p. into mice and the mice were tested for their ability to escape the shock by running to the light. In these and similar experiments statistically significant positive results were observed and the investigators claimed to have exhibited a transfer of learning. Recently, Ungar claims to have identified the memory molecule during the acquisition of dark avoidance: it is a pentadecapeptide which Ungar has named Scotophobin.

In all these transfer experiments it should be no surprise to the reader to learn that considerable difficulty has been encountered in attempting to duplicate these results in other laboratories. On theoretical grounds alone it would appear improbable since (a) the injected material in which the information is presumed to be encoded in a biopolymer such as a protein or nucleic acid must pass the blood-brain barrier intact. (b) This macromolecule must seek out the precise neuronal network that is concerned with the stimulus-specific learned behavior. (c) This macromolecule must then somehow be incorporated as an intact molecule.

On the more pragmatic side, the major criticism in these experiments is that there are innumerable variables in training and testing. Further, what is referred to as a simple T- or Y-maze, one of the commonly used tests, is far from simple according to experimental psychologists.

3. *Interruption.* Procedures for interfering with the consolidation of information generally involve the intracranial injection of antibiotics that disrupt protein synthesis. Puromycin, cycloheximide, and acetoxycycloheximide are the popular agents that have been employed. Some similar experiments have also been done with nucleic acid inhibitors such as actinomycin D, which inhibits DNA-dependent RNA polymerase, and 8-azaguanine, which is incorporated into nucleic acids. Both of these agents will, of course, subsequently interfere with protein biosynthesis.

For an individual not working in this area it is difficult to relate a coherent account of these experiments with protein inhibitors. Not only are the experimental conditions constantly varied but interpretations change with each publication and the committed investigators in this area are not entirely in agreement on acceptable criteria.

If we take experiments with puromycin as an example these difficulties will be readily apparent. Puromycin, an analogue of transfer RNA, blocks protein synthesis by disrupting polysomes; it is released from polysomes as a peptidyl-puromycin. Flexner and Flexner injected puromycin into both temporal lobes of mice which had been trained in a T-maze. In their initial report they found no effect on memory but in a subsequent paper they showed that whereas short-term memory was unimpaired, long-term memory was blocked. In a succeeding paper, the Flexners then showed that the memory could be restored by an intracerebral injection of saline. More recently they observed the saline injections were ineffective in restoring memory if the puromycin was given either before or immediately after training. Most recently, they reported that if instead of injecting saline two days after the administration of puromycin they wait five or ten days, then the saline restores memory.

With respect to the mechanism of action of puromycin, the Flexners suggest that the memory block is due to the presence of peptidyl-puromycin in the brain.

Cohen and Barondes found that cycloheximide prevented the effect of puromycin in blocking memory in mice. Cohen and Erwin demonstrated that the intracranial injection of puromycin produced seizure-like EEG changes in the hippocampal region. By contrast, cycloheximide had no such effect. Cohen and Barondes later found that this seizure effect of puromycin could, in fact, be blocked by previous administration of cycloheximide. Further, the anticonvulsant diphenylhydantoin not only blocked the abnormal EEG effect of puromycin but also prevented the inhibiting effect of puromycin on memory.

Cohen and Barondes found that acetoxycycloheximide injected intracerebrally to mice trained for light-dark discrimination produced no loss in memory for up to three hours after the training session. However, six hours after training, memory was impaired in the mice trained to a 9 out of 10 correct response criterion. If training was then continued to a criterion of 15 out of 16 correct responses, there was no amnesic effect of the drug. That is to say, overtraining abolishes the drug effect. In another experiment these authors found that when mice that were trained to discriminate between left and right, rather than light-dark as above, were injected with acetoxycycloheximide, no impairment of memory was observed when they were trained to the usual criterion of 9 out of 10 correct responses. The "overtraining" explanation may in fact be merely a temporal factor in the action of the antibiotic since Squire and Barondes have recently shown that cycloheximide initially produces amnesia but a spontaneous recovery of memory occurs after three days.

Agranoff trained goldfish to swim over a hurdle toward a light in order to escape a shock, and found that puromycin, as well as acetoxycycloheximide and actinomycin D, blocks this long-term memory: no effect on short-term memory by these agents was noted. Cytosine arabinoside, a DNA synthesis inhibitor, had no effect on short- or long-term memory.

What can one conclude from these experiments with agents that block protein synthesis? First of all it is clear with puromycin that one is dealing with an agent that does more than inhibit protein synthesis. Although no other effects of the other protein inhibitors have been reported as yet, it is more than probable that they occur. The student must be aware that there is no such thing as a "pure" drug that has only one biochemical action. There is an aphorism that every drug has two actions: the one you know about and the one you don't. It can, therefore, be concluded that it is too early to make conclusions about the relationship between protein synthesis and memory. That such an association may exist is not denied: it just is not yet proven. Second, it is also clear that the complexities in the type of training given, the training period, the timing of the injections of drugs, the kind of drug, the site of injection, and a host of other variables are such that meaningful experiments are difficult. Finally, on a more personal note, it is not without considerable irritation that one reviews the literature on this subject because of the abundance of premature publications that manifest questionable critical judgment.

4. *Correlation* between learning and biochemical changes in cells. This approach is exemplified by the work of Hydén and his colleagues. In a succession of studies, animals were either rotated on a turntable, trained to balance on a steel wire, or trained to transfer handedness (e.g. to use the right paw instead of the left). Then, the biochemistry of cells from the "appropriate" area of the brain in experimental and control animals was determined.

In the rotation and steel wire experiments, neurons and glia were dissected out of Dieters' nucleus; in the transfer of handedness, cells from the 5th and 6th layers of the cortex were removed. In these experiments Hydén found changes in the base pair ratios of RNA, an increase in the amount of RNA, increase in the activity of some enzymes and in total protein. Similar but not identical changes were found both in the neurons and the glia that were examined.

These experiments have been severely criticized:

1. In the dissection of neurons and glia there is contamination of one by the other. Moreover, in neurons only the perikaryon is dissected out and the remaining neuronal elements, in particular the dendritic branches which also contain RNA, are left behind.

2. The cells involved in the specific learning procedure have not been mapped out so that Hydén cannot possibly correlate learning with a biochemical change in the function of the cell or group of cells. Also the state of the cells after learning is unknown. That is, for example, did the cells taken from Dieters' nucleus of animals which were rotated have an increased or decreased rate of discharge, i.e. were they activated or depressed?

3. No attempt was made to look at the condition of dissected neurons either electrophysiologically or with an electron microscope to assess their viability.

4. Since local circulatory changes sometimes accompany stimulation of neuronal pathways *in vivo*, the biochemical changes observed by Hydén and his group may reflect increased transport of substrates rather than an association with learning.

5. If indeed new RNA were being formed it would be extremely difficult to determine it in the presence of a large mass of genetically determined, i.e. fixed, RNA. In point of fact, the finding by Hydén of increased RNA and protein indicates the nonspecificity of the biochemical changes since learning one single task should not produce a gross

change in RNA or protein that could be measured with current techniques.

In reviewing the variety of approaches that have been taken in the study of the mechanisms of memory and learning, the advantages of using simple neural preparations rather than whole animals become obvious. For example, the headless cockroach preparation appears most promising. Here a conditioned avoidance response of a leg attached to the prothoracic ganglion is used along with a yoked control preparation. The preparation "learned" to avoid a shock by retraction of the leg. It has been shown that cycloheximide can block this "learning" (though this agent may also affect performance rather than learning). Since in this preparation one can map out the motor cells within the ganglion and their connections to the leg muscles, it may be possible to establish a specific association between protein synthesis and learning. (It may seem ironic to suggest that one of the best preparations for the neurochemical study of learning is in an animal which has no head).

At the present time one can only state that protein and RNA synthesis may occur along with learning but the experiment has yet to be designed that explicitly relates these two events. The somewhat chaotic condition of this field is due not only to an inordinate amount of dross that has been presented but to monistic interpretations of data. Caveat emptor.

SELECTED REFERENCES

Agranoff, B. (1972). In *Basic Neurochemistry* (R. W. J. Albers, G. J. Siegel, R. Katzman, and B. Agranoff, Eds.), Little, Brown, Boston, p. 645.

Glassman, E. (1969). The biochemistry of learning. An evaluation of the role of RNA and protein. *Ann. Rev. Biochem. 38*, 605.

Jarvik, M. E. (1972). Effect of chemical and physical treatments on learning and memory. *Ann. Rev. Psych. 23*, 457.

Kandel, R. E., and W. A. Spencer (1968). Cellular neurophysiological approaches in the study of learning. *Physiol. Rev. 48*, 65.

McGaugh, J. L., S. F. Zornetzen, P. E. Gold, and P. W. Landfield (1972). Modification of memory systems: some neurobiological aspects. *Quart. Rev. Biophys. 5, 2.*

Moore, R. Y., A. Bjorklund, and U. Stenevi (1971). Plastic changes in the adrenergic innervation of the rat septal area in response to denervation. *Brain Res. 33*, 13.

Raisman, G. (1969). Neuronal plasticity in the septal nuclei of the rat. *Brain Res. 14*, 25.

Schmitt, F. O. (1970). *The Neurosciences—Second Study Program.* Rockefeller University Press, New York.

Squire, L. R., and S. H. Barondes (1972). Variable decay of memory and its recovery in cycloheximide-treated mice. *Proc. Nat. Acad. Sci. 69*, 1416.

# Index